Dear Readers . . .

In 1981, "The People's Friend" introduced a new feature to the magazine called "The Farmer And His Wife". It was a series of country tales told by fictional farmer John Taylor, written by Fife town planner Maurice Taylor, who drew on his memories of his own farming background to create the world of the Riggin.

Each story was illustrated by one of our most popular artists, Douglas Phillips. In his unique, lively and observant style, Doug captured the warm and homely feel of the stories perfectly, and thirty years later the series is still among the most popular features in the magazine.

This souvenir book is a chance for you to enjoy some more of our favourite stories and illustrations from "The Farmer And His Wife".

Contents

A Vanishing Way Of *Life*

Farming in Fife has faced many changes since the Taylors started out . . .

S INCE at least the Neolithic period, around 6,000 years ago, Scotland's land has been cultivated for agricultural purposes, with forests gradually and inexorably making way for arable land. But it wasn't until the 20th century that world events and advances in technology began to transform the way of life farming folk had followed for generations.

Following World War I, the prices farmers could expect for their crops and livestock slumped, and during the 1920s and 30s, when John Taylor was a boy, as much as 40% of Scottish land changed hands as the economy experienced a period of depression. No wonder he and Anne grew up to have such ▶

a strong sense of "waste not, want not".

In many ways, John and Anne's stories of life on the Riggin are a snapshot of the final days of a bygone era. Ploughing with horses began to be less common as tractors slowly took over from the early 20th century onwards, and as machinery grew ever larger, so, too, did the fields the machines worked.

By the late 1950s, a working horse was a rarity on Scottish farms, though John had fond memories of sitting astride the huge, gentle Clydesdale horses as a young boy.

The first recorded use of the name Clydesdale for the breed was in 1826, though these versatile draught horses had been used in Scotland for many years before that.

During the late 19th and early 20th centuries they were exported in large numbers across the world, including to Australia and New Zealand, where they became known as "the breed that built Australia".

But increasing mechanisation saw the number of horses used on Scottish farms decline rapidly after World War I, and soon the tractor was seen everywhere.

When it was first manufactured in 1917, the Fordson Model F was an immediate success, with three quarters of a million sold between 1917 and 1928. It was small, lightweight, mass produced and affordable, and of course was much cheaper to run and maintain than a team of horses. Even the most traditionally minded farmers quickly saw that it made life much easier, and John Taylor, ▶

Before tractors, Clydesdales were used as draught horses.

Anne was proud of her Rhode Island Red hens.

Life begins again.

too, relied heavily on the services of his old Fordson.

The Riggin of Fife where John and Anne set up home is an area of high ground in the north-east of the Kingdom. It's an area with a strong sense of community, populated by families whose roots, in many cases, go back generations.

The climate and soil are suited to arable farming, with wheat, barley, oats, turnips, potatoes and other vegetables all growing well. In fact, potatoes were grown on the Riggin, and one of Anne's jobs was to deliver them in bags around the local area in the farm buggy.

Anne and John, of course, always had a soft spot for the livestock on their farm. As a boy, John kept bantam hens – a breed called Old English Game – and later, once they were married, Anne had great success with her Rhode Island Red hens. This American breed reached the UK in 1903, and is much prized for the quantity and quality of its eggs.

Anne always had a keen business head, and when she and John were saving up to get married, she contributed to the fund by fattening and then selling runt piglets.

Over the years, the Riggin was home to milking cows and the resultant calves, and to numerous sheep. John was particularly pleased with the cross-bred Cheviot-Border Leicester flock that he raised.

The Cheviot breed originated in the Cheviot Hills and is hardy and well suited to inhospitable conditions; crossed with the versatile Border Leicester, it produces the famous "Scottish Half-bred". They were kept to heel by John's faithful Border collie, Jip.

When it came time to take the livestock to market, John's nearest sales were at Cupar. A day out at the market was a social occasion, a chance to catch up with all the news from fellow farmers and a welcome diversion from what was often quite a solitary way of life.

A much grander affair, and eagerly anticipated, was Perth Bull Sales, established in 1865, which Anne particularly enjoyed attending. In between sales, John kept up to date with developments by reading his favourite "Farmer's Weekly".

The luxury of electric light by which to do so was something John never took for granted; he remembered all too well the days of paraffin lamps, which his father used to refill on a Sunday afternoon. And the telephone, too, didn't become a feature of his family home till 1928.

It was, in many ways, and certainly by modern standards, a hard life, with long hours, back-breaking manual labour and periods of isolation. But John and Anne didn't seem to mind – for them, it was just what honest, hard-working farming folk did.

"We are fortunate," John wrote, "to be tillers of the soil and carers of the animals. It is a very satisfying life." ■

The Fife soil is perfect for growing vegetables.

Down Memory Lane

A Labour Of Love

There's no chore involved when a task brings back happy memories!

I CAME into the kitchen for my morning break and to have a look at what the postman had left.

I knew it was a Friday morning because, as I entered the kitchen, Anne had some newspapers spread on our kitchen table and was cleaning an antique, long-handled copper bed warmer, a job she does as regular as clockwork.

"John, you wouldn't credit it, but it's forty-eight years tomorrow since we bought this in Kirkby Lonsdale," she told me.

She lifted the lid and pasted inside was a note in copperplate writing.

It read, *To Anne and John with love from "Aunt" Mabel.*

The aunt was in inverted commas because she wasn't really a relation, but an adopted aunt. She and "Uncle" Jim meant as much to us as any relation.

Anne and I bought it for Aunt Mabel's kindness to us when we were down in Kirkby Lonsdale at the wedding of one of Anne's relations.

We gave it to Mabel on the Sunday night of our return – the date under the lid. Mabel was determined that on her death it was to be handed to Anne to treasure, which we both do.

Jim and Mabel were the salt of the earth. A great couple whose one regret, though they never voiced it, was that they had no family to follow on and take over their farm near Crail. They sort of adopted Anne and me. I'll tell you how it happened.

I had entered a bantam hen at Cupar Show. I think it was 1933, but I daren't ask Anne the date as she will say, "You should know." You see, it was the day I first met her.

Well, whilst the judges got down to judging the bantam entries, I went to look at the sheep pens. I was leaning over the pen of the sheep that had been awarded a first-class ticket when I heard, "Hello, John, have you entered some sheep?"

I looked up and there was big Jim Calder, a friend of Dad's.

I told him I hadn't, but hoped to one day.

I asked why the judges had given those three lambs a first ticket. In five minutes he gave me a practical lesson on how to judge sheep. He ended by telling me to come down any evening to his farm and he would go round the stock with me.

On the way home from the show on my cycle, I caught up with a young lady who had also been there. We pushed our cycles slowly up on to the Riggin. She knew my name, so I didn't like to ask hers.

I left her at their bottom farm gate, determined I would see her again.

My problem was how to find out her name. I knew the name of her dad's farm, but who could I ask without letting the cat out of the bag?

I decided to take up Jim Calder's offer to go and look over his stock. During the course of the evening, I told him about meeting the lassie from a farm near Largoward. Could he help me?

Yes, he knew the farmer and told me his name, but unfortunately he didn't know the lassie's name.

Three days later he rang and asked for me. He told me an in-calf heifer we had looked at had calved a bull. But he took the opportunity of saying, "Her name's Anne."

During our courting days, Anne and I went, most Saturday nights, to take an evening meal with them. They treated us like the children they never had.

But how did we come to give them a long-handled copper warming pan? Well, that's another story! ▥

The Path Of True Love . . .

It never runs smoothly, and I could really do with some advice!

WAS telling you how Anne and I came to be in possession of a long-handled copper warming pan. We bought it many years ago in Kirkby Lonsdale for our dear friends "Aunt" Mabel and "Uncle" Jim, but what, you might well ask, were we doing in Kirkby Lonsdale?

Well, I had booked six lambs in at the Cupar auction and, as they wouldn't be sold till after the cattle, I took a wander up the street to look for Anne, whom I'd been courting just a short while at that time.

I met up with her near the Cross and we went into a café for a cup of tea and a scone.

I could see she was bubbling over to tell me something. The girl had hardly got the teacups on the table when out it came.

Anne had received an invitation to a wedding and it was for both of us.

"Is it a local do?" I asked.

"Oh, no, it's from a cousin in Kirkby Lonsdale."

"Where on earth is Kirkby Lonsdale?" I wanted to know.

Anne explained it was a small market town near Lancaster.

"You won't be going, will you? It's too far."

"Of course I'm going, and so are you," she retorted.

I was really taken aback. No-one was telling me what I was or wasn't to do!

"Is that a fact?" I queried.

Putting some money on the table, I told Anne to pay for tea and scones out of it and stormed out of the café.

If she had just said, "John, you will come, won't you?" I have little doubt that I would have said yes, but I had to make it plain to Anne that she couldn't boss John Taylor about.

After the auction, I returned to the buggy to find her waiting beside it.

"I'm sorry, John, I didn't mean it like that," she told me apologetically.

"Well, you said it and you meant it when you said it! So I'm not coming to the wedding. It's too far and Dad would have six milkings on his own."

I left Anne almost in tears as I drove out of the car park, although I did let the window down and tried to soften the blow by saying, "I'll think about it."

Driving home, I wondered if I should call our friendship off, but I loved Anne and decided to wait and see. I would let her make the next move, but one thing was certain – I was not going to be dictated to.

As Dad and I were milking that night, I decided to ask his advice. I finished my milking and sat on my three-legged stool with my back to the byre wall, right opposite Dad, who still had his head against a cow.

"Dad, I want your advice," I began.

He handed me his bucket of milk, which I emptied and then sat back on my stool. He didn't move from where he was sitting.

I told him my problem.

I'd never known him wax so well and long before. He got on the theme that we only lived once and to be married to the "wrong 'un" would be a fate worse than death.

"Boy," he finished, "you did the right thing. Now wait and let Anne make the first move. Don't you do it, boy, or you're finished for life."

There was nothing I could do but wait. ▦

On The Right Lines

How on earth would we get to Anne's cousin's wedding?

ANNE and I had fallen out when I reckoned she'd been a bit too bossy in telling me I would be accompanying her to her cousin's wedding in Kirkby Lonsdale.

Our dear friends "Uncle" Jim and "Aunt" Mabel had engineered a meeting, and Anne and I were at least speaking again, although the prickly subject of the wedding hadn't yet been mentioned.

The subject arose from an unexpected quarter. Jim rang me.

"John, for goodness' sake, come down tonight, my life's being made unbearable," he complained.

I couldn't refuse Uncle Jim's plea. When I got there, he met me and we had a chat in the yard. Well, he talked and I listened.

Jim always was one for being forthright.

"John, if you want to marry Anne, for goodness' sake agree to go to this wedding."

What could I do when it was put like that? I agreed to go on the condition that I was asked nicely by Anne.

The phone rang next morning and Mother went to answer, as usual.

"It's her, for you," she said curtly.

In her best pleading voice, Anne asked if I would come round to their place that night. I agreed and tried not to sound as enthusiastic as I felt.

Anne must have heard the buggy coming into their yard, because she came running out of the back door.

"Let's go for a walk, John," she suggested, putting her arm through mine.

We turned up an old path to a wood which had a burn running through it on its way to the Forth. It was one of our favourite walks. She was obviously aiming to coax me into going to the wedding.

In due course, she couldn't wait any longer.

"John, you will come to the wedding, won't you?" she asked sweetly.

I didn't answer that question, but asked another.

"Anne, how would we go?"

Anne had been so full of getting me to agree to go, that a simple thing like that had never entered her head.

It was my turn to be practical.

"Our old buggy wouldn't take us to Edinburgh, let alone England."

Anne was silent for a minute.

"Let's go by train," she suggested.

"Is there a railway station at Kirkby Lonsdale?" I asked.

Anne didn't know and I certainly didn't. There was only one way to find out – go over to Kingsbarns station and see George, the station-master.

Anne explained that she wanted to take a train to Kirkby Lonsdale.

Poor George – he, like me, hadn't a clue where it was.

Undaunted, he produced a map of all the railways in Britain.

"It's near Lancaster, George," Anne proffered.

By following the west-coast line on his map, she spotted Lancaster.

"There, George," Anne said triumphantly, pointing to a spot a few miles north.

Having found Kirkby Lonsdale, George went down his map from Edinburgh to Carlisle or, as he called it, the LMS side. Next, he fetched his massive timetable.

We could see we were there for the night. ■

Time On Their Hands

Would it be best to let the train take the strain . . .?

HAD finally given in and agreed to go with Anne to her cousin's wedding in Kirkby Lonsdale – but only after she had asked me nicely!

Now we were faced with the practical problem of how to get there.

We went to ask George, the station-master at Kingsbarns station, if we could manage it by train.

As far as I can remember, the times ran something like this: leave Leuchars on the Aberdeen-London night train at twenty-five past ten. Get out at Edinburgh and get a connection for Carstairs to join the Glasgow-London train. We would reach Carstairs at twenty past one in the morning and would have to wait half an hour for the Glasgow train.

There was, so George said, a buffet at Carstairs.

"George, I don't think it would be open at twenty past one!" Anne pointed out.

He agreed.

After turning over many pages in his huge LMS timetable, George found we would arrive on a cold Carlisle platform at half past three in the morning. How to get us off the main Glasgow-London line to that wee place in the hills, Kirkby Lonsdale, caused poor George a headache.

At last he found what he was looking for. There was a stopping train leaving Carlisle at ten past six. In other words, we would have to shiver for hours in the middle of the night on a windy railway platform. We should arrive at Kirkby Lonsdale by twenty past nine the next morning – if we were on time!

"John, we can make it. The wedding's not till two o'clock," Anne said excitedly.

I had copied it all down, having had plenty of time as George struggled from page to page of his massive timetable.

I didn't say anything in front of George, who had gone to so much trouble on our behalf, but thanked him.

"A pleasure, sir," George replied.

Anne was bubbling over with the fact that we could make it, but I'm afraid I wasn't by any means as enthusiastic. To spend the night on and off trains and waiting on at least four windy stations – one for four hours – was not my idea of fun!

I said as much as we went back to Anne's place, and as you can guess, I was in her bad books once again.

I sincerely wished her cousin had forgotten all about her relatives north of the border.

Later that day, George met "Uncle" Jim when he came to collect some heifers that he was having delivered to Kingsbarns station. He told him about Anne and me wanting to go by night train from Leuchars to Kirkby Lonsdale and what it involved in changing trains.

"Plain daft, if you ask me," George had said.

Jim conveyed all this to Mabel.

We went to their place for supper on the following Sunday evening. Mabel, by careful questioning, got Anne to admit that the journey through the night promised to be horrendous.

"Look, Anne, you're not going to spend all night on the train. I'll lend you my car."

"Oh, Aunt Mabel, we couldn't borrow your car!" Anne protested.

But Mabel insisted, and we took Mabel's car home that same evening.

It looked like I was going to have to go to this wedding after all. ▨

Where Did You Get That Hat?

It's up to me to help Anne get ahead for her cousin's wedding!

IN the days before Anne and I were married, it was a long way to Kirkby Lonsdale!

An invitation to the wedding of Anne's cousin there had caused us a lot of heart-searching, to say the least. Going by train was out of the question, but when "Aunt" Mabel offered us the use of her car, Anne wrote to accept the invitation.

The next problem was what to give as a wedding present.

I suggested that Anne and her brothers and sisters make a peg rug and we would take it with us.

That idea was immediately squashed.

"John, if we take it with us, it won't be on show at the present-showing, days before the wedding."

I couldn't honestly see that it mattered, but it was worrying Anne, so I had a chat with her mum, who was a very down-to-earth person.

I told her Anne felt the present from the wild northern heathens should be on show, and should do us all credit.

She made short shrift of that. She and Anne's dad would buy a dinner service and we – Anne and I – could put a bit towards it. We could take it down with us and forget about this on-show business.

The next headache, at least for Anne, was what to wear. My Anne is very good at "running up" anything.

She asked what colour I thought she should get. I've always thought she looked best in brown, and I told her so.

She came back from Cupar with a length of material in an odd apple-green shade.

When I went to see her the following Saturday night, she brought the skirt part out for my inspection.

"How do you like it?" she asked.

"Very nice, dear." Without thinking, I added, "What are you going to wear on your head?"

Anne never goes into a church without wearing a hat.

"I'll get a hat to tone," she informed me.

Well, Anne went to Cupar, St Andrews and, I believe, Dundee, with a piece of her material, but could not find a hat.

I was walking down the street in Cupar one day when I noticed the headgear of a lady in front. It wasn't a hat, more a bonnet – with a pom-pom. I suddenly twigged how it was made. I stored the design away in the back of my mind.

"Have you got a hat to match yet?" I asked when I next went to Anne's.

I got a really filthy look and no answer.

"Have you got any of the material left?" was my next question.

"Yes," she replied.

I got her to bring me the biggest pie plate they had, as well as brown paper, scissors and pins.

Everyone, even Anne's ma, bless her, watched as I drew a circle round the plate on the brown paper. I cut it out and then divided it into six triangles. I cut a long strip of paper about four inches wide and halved it, then put it round Anne's head and pinned it where it met. Then I began to fasten the triangles of brown paper with pins.

It looked a bit odd, but everyone twigged the idea.

Well, Anne set to and made proper patterns, and in no time we had the material cut out and stitched together. Anne then made two pom-poms.

We all agreed it was a model hat. I reckoned she looked smashing, better than she would have in any hat she could have bought. ▦

On The Road To Kirkby Lonsdale

I recall the trials and tribulations – and the joys – of motoring in days gone by.

KIRKBY LONSDALE – how far was it and how did we get there by road?

That was the question Anne and I put our minds to now that we were definitely going to her cousin's wedding in that far-away town. At least, it seemed far away from the Riggin in the 1930s, when we were sweethearts!

It was agreed we should set off first thing after milking on Friday morning and drive right down to Kirkby Lonsdale.

"At least we will be there ready for the wedding the next day," Anne said.

She had booked two single rooms at the Royal Hotel.

We were given a great send-off by her family – packs of sandwiches, cakes and a flask of tea, plus wedding present. We made the Forth ferry by about half past ten that morning. There was no queue, but I was worried in case I damaged "Aunt" Mabel's car.

It was fine driving until I got to Edinburgh. Even in 1936, Princes Street with its trams was a nightmare to me compared with Cupar.

I was glad to see the open country as we left the capital behind. We drove at a steady 40 miles per hour, which was quite a speed in those days. First stop was in the wide main street of Biggar, where we had our tea and sandwiches and stretched our legs.

We went through Abington, then Crawford, then climbed slowly for miles until we got to Beattock Summit. We dropped down the other side, apparently downhill all the way to Lockerbie.

Here we parked in the square and went into a café for a cup of tea and scones. After Lockerbie, we were in a different farming world of big dairy herds. It made our few cows look as though we were playing at farming.

We went through Carlisle, which seemed much bigger than I had thought. Then came Penrith, and it was just as we were leaving that we nearly had an accident.

There was a very narrow, hump-back bridge at Eamont and you couldn't see any car coming up the other side. Well, two of us met in the middle. He kindly reversed. I thanked him.

I had heard tales of people going over the famous Shap as though they were climbing the Himalayas, terrible stories of hardship and accidents. When we reached the summit we noticed a number of cars and lorries at the roadside, many steaming from their radiators. We wondered why. We soon found out.

"Oh, John, look – watch!"

The road, as we went over the summit, dropped away, it seemed, vertically. A notice said, *Dangerous to cyclists. Engage in low gear*.

I did so and we were nearly boiling when we reached the wee bridge and cottage in the dip before we started to climb up the other side.

We stopped a few miles further on and looked down over the valley in Kendal and had more sandwiches and let the car cool down. It was a beautiful run all the way down to Kendal, then left over a stone bridge and on to Kirkby Lonsdale.

We reached our destination by half past six that evening. We didn't need to ask where the hotel was. It filled one side of the square.

Anne will never know how thankful I was to stable the car in the hotel's back yard. I put my arms around her and gave her a kiss! ■

"Thank You, Mabel"

That's exactly what Anne and I wanted to say, and we found a very unusual way of doing it.

ANNE and I had finally arrived in Kirkby Lonsdale in the north of England for her cousin's wedding. After the long drive south I was more than pleased to stable the car in the hotel yard.

We were shown to two single rooms looking over the cobbled yard at the back. Dinner, we were told, was from seven till nine p.m. I had a wash and a shave and went down to wait for Anne. She had changed into a dress I had always liked and I thought she looked beautiful.

At our reserved table for two, the waiter handed us both a menu.

We were taken aback by the choice and the four courses, but we did full justice to the unaccustomed luxury.

After coffee Anne got her coat and we went in search of the Wesleyan Methodist Chapel, where the wedding was to be held the next day. We were really taken with the fascinating main street – all stone buildings, different sizes and shapes, shops, pubs and offices in the hub of this small market town.

Anne gave my arm a squeeze.

"Glad you came, John?"

"Yes, dear."

We were both enjoying ourselves immensely.

We had noted that breakfast wasn't until half past eight. I woke up as usual at six o'clock, pulled back the curtains and went back to bed.

When we finally went in to breakfast it was a revelation – porridge, bacon, two eggs and kidney, toast, marmalade and a pot of coffee!

We found out from the lady at the desk that the bride's farm was only three miles up the valley, so we delivered our gift. Afterwards, we came back to the town and wandered along the main street, looking in the shops. We agreed that it would be nice to take Mabel a present as a thank-you for the loan of her car.

We were looking through the window of an antiques shop when Anne gave an exclamation of delight.

"We'll take her that!" she said.

It was a long-handled copper warming pan. No dithering about, we bought it on the spot. Cost, three pounds! And that, come to think of it, was what started me off on this whole extraordinary tale!

Well, we went back to the hotel with our purchase, sat in the lounge and had another pot of coffee before we went to get "dolled up" for the big "do" which had caused so much trouble.

Anne looked beautiful in her apple green suit and hat.

At the chapel we were ushered into the bride's side of the pews. The bride's mother looked round, smiled at us, then froze. How was my dear Anne to know that the bride's mother had chosen an apple-green wedding outfit, too? Anne's face was a picture.

As we sat down I got a dig in the ribs.

"We haven't got buttonholes. Everyone else has," Anne said frostily.

It wasn't a good start to the proceedings, but at least the minister was short and to the point, and we only had two hymns.

Back at the Royal Hotel, Anne changed out of her apple green and we joined the wedding party in the village hall. We all had a very good evening.

The couple left at nine o'clock and we escaped a few minutes later. We walked down, under a nearly full moon, to Devil's Bridge.

Those two days were, in the span of life, only a moment in time, but they were an interlude that Anne and I will never forget. ■

John loves driving in the countryside.

John
In Anne's
Kitchen

Anything You Can Do

Anne always seems to make it look so easy, but I find it hard to get cracking in the kitchen . . .

I WONDER if I will ever learn to keep my mouth shut . . .
I came in just after five and Anne was rolling out pastry on her
marble slab. At her side was an ovenproof dish, quite a large one,
with meat, onions and carrots just waiting for their pastry top.

"You're doing us well tonight, dear," I commented.

"John Taylor, if you think you're going to have a steak pie on a
Wednesday night, you've another think coming," she retorted.

To be honest, I didn't see why a Wednesday night was any different
from any other night, but Anne obviously did.

"Why the steak pie?" I asked.

"I thought it would be handy in the freezer if any of the family rang to
say they were coming."

I realised that our daughter, Mary, must have been on the phone.

I was right! The pair had been chatting that morning, arranging when
Mary and all the brood would be visiting Granny and Grandad. Granny
was making sure a good meal would be served up.

Knowing how loath Anne is to let anything go to waste, I made a
tentative suggestion.

"I suppose, to use the oven's heat, you'll be making an egg custard?"

"No, but you can make a lemon meringue pie, if you like."

I could have kicked myself. I'd meant to say lemon meringue pie all
along, but the words "egg custard" just sort of came out.

Anne, with the sarcasm she saves up for moments like these, had
told me to do it myself! Well, I would show her. I had watched Anne
make lemon meringue many a time, but I'd never actually helped.

I got the packet for the filling out of the larder and read the
instructions. My heart sank.

One egg, separated.

I've watched Anne juggle with an egg to get the white from the yolk,
but I'd never dared to try this tricky operation.

Anne said to double the ingredients. Oh, dear, that meant two eggs to be separated.

I broke the first egg and then deftly poured the white into a jug and the yolk into a cup.

"Beginner's luck," Anne said drily.

I wasn't so lucky with egg number two. Plop! The yolk fell into the jug for whites.

Anne laughed.

"You won't get it out without breaking it," she averred.

I got a spoon and carefully edged it round the egg yolk and it came out into the yolk cup. I grinned at Anne smugly, but didn't say a word.

The rest of the instructions presented no problems until *whisk the egg white until stiff.*

I whisked and whisked and whisked, but just couldn't get it to come into peaked mountains as Anne said it should.

Anne made the pastry base and poured in my custard, then put on its meringue top. It went into the cool oven to use up the heat.

It's now gone into the deep freeze for when the family come. I'd hoped we'd sample it there and then.

Still, I don't mind too much as I've achieved something I never thought I would – to separate the white of an egg from the yolk. ■

Smoke Gets In Your Eyes

I have discovered another shortcut not worth taking!

'VE always said we should go out more on a Saturday night. Perhaps the word "more" is wrong. Put it this way, we couldn't go out less as the moon would turn blue if we did!

Just to show you how often we go out, say, to the pictures – many years ago now, I ran into the retired manager of our local cinema.

We chatted and then he said, "John, do you know how often you have been to the pictures in the last twenty-five years?"

I hadn't a clue, so he told me – twice.

Once my daughter took me, he said, to "The Sound Of Music", and I only came because I thought the film was to be "The Bridge On The River Kwai"!

Anne and I always keep saying, too, that we should go to our local theatre. I wish we had gone one particular Saturday night.

"John, the stove hasn't been drawing well all day," Anne complained.

I checked. Sure enough, there was no draught. It looked like a ball of soot might be stuck halfway up the chimney.

"We must get it swept."

I offered to do it the following week.

Anne gave me one of her looks. She wanted it done now.

I had at least offered. And my method was cheap. Just go out on to the brae for some dry gorse or whin, stuff it up the chimney, set it alight and hope it didn't set the chimney too much on fire.

I pointed out to Anne that that was how we did it at home and I bet her mother did, too.

I was promptly told no; they had a real sweep. To be honest, that was too fine a name for him. He was the local odd-job man, who had a very long brush which he also used for clearing blocked drains.

Anyway, in the end, expediency won the day. We used my crude "burn it and hope" method, there and then.

All was going well till Anne, for some reason best known to her, opened the door to the stove and there was a back blast. The ball of

34

soot came down the chimney like a shot out of a gun!

Anne shut the door quickly, but the damage had been done. She now looked like she'd been down the mines – black all over!

That would not have been so bad in itself, but the kitchen was swimming in smoke and soot.

Anne's beautifully kept white wood refectory table was all grey and smudgy. She could have wept.

Seven o'clock on a Saturday night and a room full of soot.

Once she had got over the initial shock, though, Anne became all action. So did I.

"John, get those curtains down. Put a line up and come back – no going off, now. Take the rugs outside."

Orders were delivered in quick succession.

"Get the steps and lift everything off the pot-rail – wipe it."

Curtains were on the line in no time. The kitchen table was washed so that all the bits off the pot-rail could go on it after washing.

Anne even washed the walls and threatened to distemper the ceiling.

At half past ten I suggested we have a cup of something. I was getting fed up and wanting a break. We had milky hot chocolate and it tasted . . . well, sooty, really.

There was one thing we didn't do and that was to open the front of the fire. We let it die out and arranged for a real sweep to come and put his brush down the chimney on Monday.

We should have gone out to something that Saturday night – it would have saved us a lot of toil, sweat and tears. ▪

A Sting In The Tail

I was only trying to be helpful, but I wish I'd left my ideas in cold storage!

I'M in trouble.

That's not unusual. I'm always in trouble over wanting to help. That's the way I think of it, anyway, but Anne doesn't see it quite like that.

If I would just get on and do my job – the farm – she would look after the house and the meals, thank you very much.

It's the meals bit that worries me. I love my food. No wonder I'm eighteen stone, Anne says, the way I put food by.

But to get back to, "I'm in trouble".

It was Sunday night. We had been sitting watching "Songs Of Praise". Monday follows Sunday, and during the last hymn my mind went not to the words "Give no thought to the morrow", but to my own up-to-date version: "I wonder what we are having for lunch tomorrow?"

In the days when the family were all at home there was no need to wonder. In those far-off, happy days Anne always had a joint of something on a Sunday and, therefore, cold meat on Monday.

Now there's only the two of us we very seldom have a slap-up soup, meat, veg and sweet for Sunday lunch.

During the last hymn, I got round to thinking about an oxtail; my eyes shut, savouring the smell of oxtail simmering away on the stove. I love a tail-pot. Anne says if I go into a butcher's I come out with an oxtail plus. I'll tell you about the plus later.

I knew we had at least two tails in the deep-freeze in the dairy, so after the last hymn I went to get one out.

To save Anne work on the Monday I scraped some carrots and then peeled about half a dozen onions.

The door opened.

"What do you think you're doing?"

I had to try to sound innocent.

"Just trying to help you, dear. I knew you would be busy tomorrow, so I was doing the vegetables."

"What are you having with them?"

"An oxtail."

That was when I got the remark about me running the farm and she'd run the home.

"Many women would get a divorce on the grounds of interference in the kitchen."

That was a new one on me. I don't think it would stick.

"Mrs Taylor, did you say your husband was peeling vegetables for you? You should think yourself lucky. No divorce, madam. Case dismissed, with costs to Mr Taylor."

"What were you having for lunch tomorrow, dear?" I asked when she had paused for breath.

"I hadn't thought, but I've never failed to come up with something, have I?"

I can't dispute that fact, but I still like to know what I'm having and there's nothing better than an oxtail and plenty of vegetables and gravy.

Give Anne her due, next morning she put all my Sunday night bits and pieces – carrots, onions, potatoes, and part of a turnip, plus the oxtail – in our big pan and let it simmer away.

By lunchtime, ten minutes past twelve, it was all – plus chutney – out of this world.

The flesh fell away from the bone and I really felt we had had a meal. Not good for the figure, but oh, so satisfying.

I said I'd tell you about going into the butcher's and coming out with an oxtail "plus". Well, the plus, unfortunately, is round my waistline! ■

Some Like It Hot!

I fear I'm in the soup once again after invading Anne's kitchen!

'M in trouble again! To put you in the picture, you'll have guessed by now how much I enjoy messing about in the kitchen. Ever since I was a small boy, I've been interested in cooking.

I think I was about eleven when Mother went to visit a relative, leaving Dad and me to fend for ourselves for a few days. I was chief cook and bottle-washer while she was away.

I remember it was late summer at the time and the orchard was laden with Victoria plums. We had them with custard. I could make that for breakfast, dinner and tea.

One day I thought I'd make a soup. I got down one of Mother's recipe books and looked up Scotch broth.

I read it, but didn't know what stock was, and it didn't tell me, so I just put lots of vegetables in a pan and boiled them. Imagine the results!

Give my dad his due, he ate them without a word.

But to come back to my being in trouble.

Well, Anne's weekly magazine arrived as usual, but that week it featured a special cookery pull-out.

I enjoy reading recipes and looking at the photographs, which make you want to get up and make them straight away.

It was a scorching hot day on the Riggin, and when I came in from the farm I had a shower and we'd cold tongue and a salad for tea.

After tea we sat in the lounge, which is most unusual when we're on our own, but it was the coolest room in the house.

I picked up Anne's new magazine and turned to the cookery pull-out.

The heading *Some Like It Cool* took my eye that hot evening.

It was recipes for cold soups, which seemed just the ticket during that hot weather.

I decided I'd make a soup and, without telling Anne, I made a mental note of what I needed to buy when I went into Cupar on Tuesday. I bought all the ingredients and managed to hide them from Anne.

I knew she was going to a WRI meeting in Anstruther on Wednesday evening, so I'd have the kitchen to myself.

As soon as the car was out of our yard gate I set to work.

It took longer than I'd anticipated, and unfortunately Anne's WRI meeting didn't last as long as I'd hoped.

I was so absorbed in what I was doing that I didn't hear the back door open.

"John, what are you doing?" Anne asked in amazement.

I always believe in telling the truth.

"Making a cold soup," I told her.

"John, if you look after the farm, I'll look after the soup," Anne replied as usual. But I knew from her tone of voice that she was quite amused.

She came across, got a spoon and tried my cold soup.

"What are those green bits?" she asked after sampling it.

"Fresh parsley, dear."

"It would have looked better without it," she said.

Anne can be my hardest critic, but most of the time I have to agree with her.

"Still," she went on cautiously. "I must admit, it's very good."

We had half of it the following day, while the other half went into the deep-freeze.

My heart swelled. I wasn't in trouble after all and, what's more, Anne actually liked my soup, which, believe it or not, I really enjoyed making.

You can't beat the simple things in life. ■

The Proof Of The Pudding

It has been ready since November, but I am finally allowed to sample the great delicacy!

DID you ever find out what a ton of hen feathers looks like?" Anne came out with this as she dished out her delicious Christmas pudding. It was a reminder of one Wednesday evening in November . . .

It was about seven o'clock when Anne mentioned the ton of feathers for the first time. What prompted the daft question was a pile of breadcrumbs rising high on her scales.

"John, there's only six ounces there! Keep going, darling, you have ten more to weigh."

I knew then it was going to be one of those daft nights, when it would be one o'clock at least before we got to bed . . .

Anne's a great one for getting on with something when the spirit moves her. And that includes making the Christmas pud.

The spirit seems to insist that Anne's ideas are best executed in the evening. It's then that she has someone to help with the menial tasks. Read, fetch, carry, weigh, get out pans, wash up or put away. Not to mention, "Oh, darling, give the sink a good wash."

"Someone" often wishes he could float away down the sink, but he obeys before going back to his paper!

We were having tea when the spirit first spoke.

"John, help me to make a Christmas pudding tonight," Anne said out of the blue as she poured the tea.

I couldn't find an excuse to go anywhere else, so I agreed. Our first problem was that Anne couldn't remember which recipe book she had used last year. She got out the one from the Young Farmers.

"John, there's no recipe for Christmas pudding!"

She handed me the book and I checked.

"There is, but it's called plum pudding – see, on page fifty-eight." I peered. "Why is it called a plum pudding? There isn't a plum in it!"

"Just for that, you can read the ingredients!" I was told.

As soon as I started, I realised why she wanted someone to read out the bits and pieces that went into a plum – not Christmas – pudding. There were 21 things in all!

"Right, you double everything. I want to make two."

"OK. We'll do sixteen ounces of breadcrumbs first."

Looking back, what we should have done was to put a loaf on the scales and weigh it. But we didn't. Anne cut it up and then put it on her old-fashioned, but very accurate, scales. The dish isn't big, so Anne was weighing four ounces, putting it into a bowl, then weighing four more, etc. It all took time. It was as the heat was growing that she came out with the phrase, never to be forgotten:

"I wonder what a ton of hen feathers looks like."

Eventually, we crumbled and weighed 16 ounces of breadcrumbs. We assembled the rest and then we mixed . . . and mixed . . .

By then it was eleven o'clock at night!

"I'll just put them on the stove, John. Will you come down at two to see they haven't run out of water?"

I gave her a look.

Anne agreed to leave the boiling and simmering operation until the next day, but it was still midnight before I finally crawled into bed.

Now it's Christmas, and I've sampled the result. What is my verdict? Delicious – and well worth all the trouble! ▦

A Sticky Problem

I'm not the only one
with an eye for a bargain . . .

IT was the third week in September – a Saturday afternoon, to be exact. A widow from one of the wee houses near the beach was in hospital recovering from a recent operation.

Her late husband had helped Anne with the garden, and since then she'd always had a soft spot for the couple.

Would I go with Anne to visit her?

I don't like city traffic, but agreed to go anyway.

I was glad we went. The poor soul hadn't had many visitors and was as pleased as Punch to show us off to the other patients in the room. Afterwards we went to St Andrews.

September is the best month for buying home-grown celery. Oh, you can get it earlier, but it's usually tough and stringy.

I like to nibble at celery. I buy a stick, tear it apart, wash it and put it in a jug in the kitchen near Anne's salt-holder.

On my way out of the kitchen, I grab a stick of celery, dip it in the salt jar and go on my way down the yard chewing.

Anyway, to get to St Andrews. I drew up the car at the greengrocer's and told Anne I was going in for a few bunches of celery.

"Do you want anything?" I asked her.

"I'll come in for plums."

Yes, he had beautiful Victoria plums, the greengrocer told us.

"Will they come down in price?" Anne asked, looking at him shrewdly.

"Yes, they might."

The price was 40 pence a pound and it was nearly five o'clock on Saturday night. He'd too many crates of Victoria plums for that time on a Saturday. By Monday morning I guessed he wouldn't get anywhere near that price for them.

Anne was about to walk out of the shop and wait for a fall in price.

"Mrs Taylor, I'll do a deal with you," he called. "If you'll take a crate, you can have them for twenty pence a pound."

Anne fell for his offer. I thought I was the only sucker who fell for

so-called bargains.

Anne left feeling well pleased with her bargain and dashed into the nearby grocer's to buy sugar.

We arrived home at the Riggin about six, Anne carrying sugar, me the crate of plums. She looked into the crate and, as women always seem to do, sampled one.

"These won't keep till Monday, they're over-ripe," she said. "Look up a recipe, John."

I got down the recipe book we bought years ago at the Young Farmers Stand at the Royal Highland Show. I turned to the plum jam recipe and read it through. It seemed too simple for words.

There was no peace that Saturday night. We wiped the plums, split them, put them into two large bowls, in layers, with sugar.

The two large jam pans with sugar and plums were brought to the boil and the aroma that came from them was mouth-watering.

"How long does it say they have to boil?" Anne asked.

"It doesn't, dear."

Anne grabbed the book. It didn't say.

"Playing for safety," was Anne's reply.

Thank goodness it set and we had sufficient jars and covers to take all Anne's Saturday-night bargain.

There's a wee problem – when are we going to eat all that plum jam? I suppose it can go to our bring-and-buy sale in aid of the church fabric fund if we don't manage it all! ■

The Cupboard Was Bare

I can recall a time when sticky fingers got me into a bit of a jam!

"WHO'S been in the lemon curd?" Anne asked as she lifted a nearly-empty lemon curd jar off the jam shelf.

It was a daft question, really, because there's now only the two of us. It was bound to be me.

I'll tell you what happened. One night I was looking round for something to put between two pieces of well-buttered bread. I couldn't see anything in the meat line; there was cheese, which I love, but – according to my wife – it makes me snore. Then my gaze came to rest on the half-empty lemon curd jar.

It made a very tasty sandwich, so I had another. Hence there wasn't much left in the jar.

Two elderly ladies were coming for tea and Anne intended making a sponge cake, sandwiched with lemon curd. Oh, dear, was I in trouble!

I offered to slip to the village in the hope that they had a pot of curd. If not it would have been accelerator pedal hard down to St Andrews. Anne wouldn't hear of it, but harped on about me and my sandwich.

"Must get the vet to look you over when he comes and give you something for your tapeworm." Anne can be very sarcastic sometimes.

I remember my dear granny used to make lemon curd so, when Anne had gone out, I got down a cookery book and looked up a recipe.

There it was, page 233 – *Lemon Curd: 4 lemons, 4 eggs, 1 lb caster sugar, 8 oz butter.* Delicious!

When I was next in St Andrews I went looking at lemons – they were 12p each in one supermarket, 10p in another and 5 for 25p in a greengrocer. That seemed more like it to me, but I only wanted four.

I've noticed that when Anne has been buying apples and oranges, she sometimes buys a lemon. It sits there on the fruit stand getting smaller and smaller each day till it looks really dejected. In the end, Anne cuts it in half and pours boiling water over it for a lemon drink.

The young lady said I could have four for 20p.

"What are those for?" Anne asked as I put them on the table.

"Lemon curd," I explained.

For a moment I thought she was going to explode, but in the end she laughed.

"John – you're hopeless – how much will they make?"

I had no idea, but said, "Ten pots."

"If it makes two, you'll be lucky," Anne retorted. But, give Anne her due, she said if I would help after supper, she would make it.

My job was to grate the lemon rind and squeeze out the juice. The recipe told us to put the sugar and butter in a double saucepan over hot water. Well, I searched everywhere and I couldn't find our double saucepan, so we substituted a Pyrex bowl in a big pan of boiling water. There was steam everywhere.

The next instruction from the book was to stir it until the mixture was smooth, thick and creamy.

Anne stirred and stirred – it was, so she said, like stirring calf porridge.

I must have used too big a grater as there were bits of lemon. We had to put it through a sieve to get rid of the rind.

It thickened but, believe it or not, we ended up with two one-pound pots.

I expected Anne to say, "I told you so", but she resisted temptation.

Well, was it worth it for all that steam, washing-up and stirring over a hot stove – for two pots? It looks and tastes good, but there's not much scope for a before-bed sandwich with only two pots, is there?

Anne is a most economical sort and the sieved rind is going into the pudding tomorrow. ■

The kitchen is the heart of the home, according to John!

Family Matters

Old-fashioned Wisdom

Things have changed a lot since my grandfather's day – including manners!

WINTER always makes me long for spring. I suppose it's the same for everyone. I was thinking of a particularly good spring a couple of years ago, when I remembered how I came across a curlew's nest in a rough area on the farm. There were four eggs in the nest – a hollow in the ground lined with a few bits of grass.

Anne and I went to look every day in the hope of seeing young curlews, but one day there were four broken egg shells and no chicks. I knew they had left the nest as soon as they were born, but we had hoped to see them before they fled to the rushes and bracken.

For some reason it made me think of my grandfather, who knew all there was to know about wild birds – their calls, their habits, their young.

It's that sort of old-fashioned countryside knowledge that we are losing, sad to say. In the days when Grandad farmed, they walked through the fields behind the plough horses. Life was lived at a slower pace then, with much more time for observing nature.

Grandad was a real honest, salt-of-the-earth farmer who never owed anyone a penny. I remember he used to insist on drinking tea from his saucer. I can imagine what Anne would say if I tried that!

Anyway, Anne came back one day from visiting a friend in Crail, who had a bird table. Anne was thrilled with the birds that came to it.

Well, if my dear Anne wanted a bird table, yours truly could oblige.

As soon as we had finished our supper, I went down to our tractor shed, got a stake, made a flat top and, hey presto.

We agreed a position about 12 feet from the window. I got a crowbar, made a hole, and in no time had her bird table in position.

Anne had hardly got the back door shut, after putting out some crumbs on the table, when its first visitor was a robin. It became obvious as we watched it that our farmyard was its territory.

Well, that robin became Anne's robin, despite the fact that he could chase any other bird off the table if he was enjoying his meal. Soon, though, by putting no crumbs on the table, but on the step, Anne got him to come regularly to our back door for his breakfast.

As we were sitting on our own round the stove that evening, Anne and I talked about the robin and its red breast.

I always thought it got its red breast from flying down from the top of the Cross to pick a thorn out of Jesus's head, and a drop of blood fell on its breast.

Anne, though, said that wasn't how it had got its red breast at all. Her grandfather had told her differently. Robin, so he said, had been sitting on a rafter in the stable at Bethlehem, where Jesus was lying in a manger, when he noticed that the fire in the grate was going out. He thought if the fire went out, the newborn babe would be cold, so he flew down and fanned the dying embers with his wings.

His wings made the fire glow so brightly that it scorched him and gave him the red breast.

My grandfather had something to say about robins, too.

"Never kill a robin, boy. If you do, your cows will give sour milk!"

Anne and I noticed that on eight of the Christmas cards we got that year there was a robin looking such an angel. But he is no angel – at least ours wasn't, as you'd have seen if you'd watched him drive everything else off Anne's bird table! ■

Like Granny Used To Make

Granny always made sure we were well fed on Christmas Eve . . .

MY granny on my mother's side was a real granny. She was always dressed in a long black skirt that didn't quite touch the ground. There was always an apron over the skirt . . .

I lost a dear friend when she died. She brought me up.

I wasn't really wanted. Could it have been because I cried for the first six months of my life? Anyway, I was packed off to Granny's and I stopped crying! She fed me, clothed me and, most important, loved me.

My cot was the bottom drawer of a bow-fronted mahogany chest of drawers. It was summer and during the day it was put outside on a slab near the back door of their farmhouse.

Anne and I have two ostrich eggs which were brought back from Australia by Granny. She and my grandad had gone there in the depression at the end of the last century. My mother was born in Australia and the family came back before WWI and set up in farming.

Every Christmas Eve, Dad, Mum and I went to Gran's for dinner.

Gran's youngest daughter never married, but stayed at home to "do" for her mother. She was a good cook and so houseproud I didn't dare go in the back door without taking my shoes off!

That Christmas Eve dinner was a ritual. First we had soup from a knap bone and vegetables. Then it was a meat hot-pot.

They had a big brown earthenware pot with a lid. It was filled with meat, potatoes, carrots, leeks, etc., in alternate layers until it reached the top. I suppose they added stock so it didn't burn.

Half an hour or so before it was taken out of the oven, the lid was removed so that the top layers of potatoes browned.

Finally we had a Christmas pudding with no burning brandy. Granny was TT! And the white sauce was definitely not out of a packet.

In the plum pudding was a few silver threepenny bits, wrapped in greaseproof paper.

Anne decided she wanted to add silver to her Christmas puddings.

We had a lot of five shilling pieces, but they were too big. Could I get any threepenny bits?

I tried the bank. Give the young tellers their due, they were polite, but looked blank. I bet they thought they had a nut-case on the other side of the counter!

I came out of the bank and saw that a gentleman had set up a stall. He had odd pieces of pottery, books, jewellery — and coins.

"Any silver threepenny pieces?"

"Yes."

"How much?"

"Fifty pence."

I did a mental calculation.

If an old shilling was worth five new pence, then sixpence was worth two and a half pence. So an old threepence was worth one and a quarter new pence . . . Fifty pence for one and a quarter pence didn't make sense — even for Anne's Christmas pud!

But Anne is never beaten. She wrapped some shiny new twenty-pence pieces in greaseproof paper.

I smiled on Christmas Day as I watched her make sure that the youngest member of the family got his silver coin.

Grannies are great, aren't they? The one I'm married to doesn't wear a long skirt, modesty bodice and apron — but she gives out love and kindness, just as mine did.

Oh, by the way, we still have the bow-fronted chest of drawers . . . ▨

Don't Teach Your Granny To Boil Eggs

But that's exactly what my ten-year-old granddaughter did try to do!

I HAVE just left the kitchen in a hurry. I had to. It happened so simply. Our only granddaughter, ten-year-old Jane, was staying with Granny.

I was there also, but quite rightly, it is always Granny's house as far as the grandchildren are concerned.

They had been down the field to the quarry and the hens. A great treat – Jane had gathered the eggs.

Granny asked what she would like for tea.

"An egg, please, Granny."

As Granny popped two brown eggs in the pan, a very serious ten-year-old spoke up.

"Granny, if you want to boil them right, I think I should tell you that you will have to time them for three minutes. I learned that at school the other day."

It was at that point that I hurried from the kitchen.

We had a good laugh about it when she had gone to bed. It somehow did not dawn on Jane that Granny had been dealing with eggs in every conceivable way for over 50 years!

We got to chatting about eggs.

Anne's dad used to bring home plovers' eggs, which Anne said were very rich.

You weren't breaking the law by taking them in those days – but I still think it was a cruel thing to do.

Anne's family, I'm sure, thought nothing about it. They were the fruits of the earth, like mushrooms, rabbits and anything else that ran, flew or grew on their farm.

Anne decided she wanted to make a cake for "the boys" – our

three grandsons.

It's called a rum cake, although it has no rum in it. She got the recipe from a friend who had written it on a piece of paper – one we had lost for the umpteenth time.

I was given the job of going through all the various recipe books to see if I could find it. I had been ages looking through "Mrs Beeton's Cookery And Household Management" when Anne came to see what I was doing.

I was reading about how to deal with plovers' eggs.

Fancy, Mrs B had three recipes for the eggs.

I came across something else which I didn't much fancy – five ways of dealing with larks.

People refer to the "good old days". In those days it was refined to serve larks. I'm glad they were not all exterminated to tempt "refined" palates, otherwise we wouldn't have them today living up on our top land.

They rise in front of me and climb vertically to a great height, singing all the time. I used to stop to watch their climb, but now I am afraid I cannot follow them, although I can still listen to their joyous song.

Who could think of killing 24 of those messengers of music to use in lark pie?

Granny's White Jug

Anne might call me sentimental, but I know a treasure when I see one . . .

"HOW do you like that?" I placed a small white jug on the kitchen table.

"Did an old flame give it to you?" Anne asked tartly.

"No, I bought it."

"Whatever for? We have hundreds of jugs!"

Luckily, Anne didn't ask the price and I wasn't telling her, or I would have been branded a sentimental old fool . . .

You see, I'd been coming back from Cupar and parked the buggy in Ceres. I wanted something at the grocer's, but as I was parked opposite an antiques shop, I crossed over and glanced in the window.

I saw the wee white jug on a shelf. The memories it brought back . . . I just couldn't resist it.

It's difficult to describe – white, less than two inches high, partly fluted, partly plain, in triangles. On the bottom, in a shield, is the word Shelley then an "R," then "1,702,171". (I wonder if over a million of them have been made.)

"Really, John, why did you buy it?"

"For mint sauce."

Anne gave me one of those looks that means she often isn't certain if I am, as they say, quite the full shilling.

"Make a cup of tea and I'll tell you why I really bought it," I said.

It was all to do with Granny, on my mother's side, who died about 45 years past. I have vivid recollections of her in her spotless cottage.

She always bought in a big way. Salt was purchased in a block about two feet long and a foot wide. I helped to grind it down and put it in brown earthenware jars.

A bigger jar was used for pickling eggs when they were less than a penny each in the summer. I remember that the lime always left a rim round the edge of the jar.

Flour was bought in half-hundredweights. The white bags it came in were duly washed and used as pillowcases. Granny's pillows were

always beautifully soft – full of duck and hen feathers.

Granny made her own salad dressing with, I suppose, her cheap summer eggs, cream, and vinegar that she bought in big brown earthenware jars with a neck, a cork and a spout.

The vinegar was a most important commodity. Granny often used to cook herring in it, in the oven next to the fire. Herring was inexpensive and, cooked or pickled in vinegar, it was delicious.

In those days mutton was also cheap and we had it more often than beef. In the corner of Grandad's garden was a veritable forest of mint. I was given the job, when very young, of chopping up the mint leaves finely on Gran's chopping board.

These, plus sugar and vinegar, made mint sauce, which went into yet more big jars. When it was put on the table, though, it was always in a little white fluted jug less than two inches high.

Granny had many jugs of different sizes, but I loved that wee jug, which I always associated with lamb and mint sauce – and Granny.

That was why I bought its twin in Ceres that Tuesday.

So Anne might think me a sentimental old fool, but never mind – I will treasure, for dear Granny's sake, my wee white jug. ■

Fashion Flair

I have turned into a trendsetter – to my granddaughter's dismay.

OH, Grandad, it's not done nowadays."

The remark was made in a very kindly way by our granddaughter when I'd found what I thought was a good solution to her problem.

True, she hadn't asked for my well-meant advice. I just gave it to her – free.

The problem centred around her finding a new dress.

She's fourteen, but if you ask me she's too old for her years. They all seem to be old for their years these days, far more grown up than I'm sure my Anne was at that age.

Anyway, apparently she has lots of parties to attend for which she felt she must have a new dress.

Anne keeps stressing to the grandchildren that money doesn't grow on trees and our granddaughter had been told that she wouldn't get a new evening dress this year.

Her protests are still ringing in my ears.

"But, Mum, I've five more parties to go to," she wailed. "I can't go in the same dress every time."

This protest was followed by the name of some girl who has a different dress for each occasion.

We had the same with our own daughter. All the other girls had more shoes, more dresses, and so on.

That night, Anne was telling me how she'd pleaded with her mum when she was seventeen to get a dress like a girl on an adjoining farm and go to dances on a Saturday night.

"You just wait, my lass, the bailiffs will walk into that farm soon enough," was all the answer she got from her mum.

Our granddaughter's problem was now how to make her old evening dress look like a new one.

For that reason, she and her mum had come here to get Granny's advice.

It was a long, black dress. I think I've heard Anne call them ball gowns. To my mind, it was too low at the top.

I watched as they held up bits of coloured material against it to make it look different.

An idea came to me. I picked up a long piece of material and folded it into a kind of sash. Then I put it over one of her shoulders and down to one side. To my mind it looked fine and you forgot the black dress below.

That was when the famous remark, which I'll remember for the rest of my life, was made.

"Oh, Grandad, it's not done nowadays."

How was I to know that sashes were out and had been, apparently, for 20 years at least?

Anne and I once went to a Highland Ball at the request of our daughter, and all the ladies there wore sashes. They really suited them, too.

I tried to explain that she'd be setting a fashion, but she wasn't convinced.

"Oh, Grandad, it's not done nowadays."

I suppose I'd better stick to farming! ▮

Just A Quick Word

I am out of answers when my daughter phones me!

ANNE is the custodian of that infernal machine, the telephone, in our house. I always hate talking on the telephone so I leave it to Anne whenever I can.

Our daughter, Mary, knows this, and if she wants to speak to me she chooses her times very carefully.

Anne always feeds her hens at about six in the evening, so Mary rang one evening about six, knowing Anne would be out.

I misguidedly answered it. I should have let it ring and whoever it was would have thought we were both out. If it had been of vital importance, they'd have rung later.

I picked it up and started to give our number. I'd just got as far as the first two numbers when I was interrupted.

"Dad, I know that's your number." It was Mary on the line.

"Mother's out, dear," I informed her.

"I thought she would be, that's why I rang now, otherwise I'd never get hold of you. I was just wondering if there's anything you'd particularly like for your birthday?"

My birthday – I won't say which one – was in a week's time.

"Mary, I don't want anything," I told her.

"But, Dad, we want to give you something."

"Please, just send me a card and wish me good health, that's all I want," I insisted.

She tried for a little longer to get some ideas from me, but I didn't have any.

"Dad, you are hopeless." She sighed finally. "Well, I just hope you like what we choose. Good night."

And with that the phone went dead. I listened for a while, but no-one was on the other end.

When you're over three score years, all you want is good health, but the family don't seem to realise this.

I know they want to give me something, but I can't tell them what.

In Anne's case, she always says, "Oh, dear, just give me a plant."

And they do, which is fine because Anne's got green fingers and we have plants everywhere, even in the bathroom.

There was a time when I always asked them to send me a shirt, but now I have so many of them, still in their Cellophane covers, that I'll never get through them all in my lifetime.

The boys, Mary's family, have got the hang of what I want. They know there's nothing I enjoy more than a good read.

Last birthday one of them gave me two books which I thoroughly enjoyed.

I must admit that I have a great fascination for books. I just wish Anne shared my love for the printed word.

There's a snag, however, and that is where to keep them? I now have six open bookcases which are all full in our third bedroom-cum-office, library or, as my granddaughter very pleasingly called it, "Grandad's word factory."

What I don't think Anne knows is that I saw a furniture dealer in St Andrews who was selling up so I bought two more bookcases. They are stored in one of our outbuildings at the moment.

I'd like to say a big thank you to a dear aunt, now long dead, who put in the pillowcase at the bottom of my bedstead, one Christmas Eve, that famous book "Robinson Crusoe."

I have read it and reread it and I still have it.

Might I suggest that if you're ever in any doubt about what to give someone for a gift, give them a book. They're sure to love it – especially children. ▪

Ask The Family

I recall testing times with my grandson's homework . . .

THE phone rang at seven-thirty on Friday night. Anne went to answer.

"Is that you, Christopher?"

"Is Grandad there?"

Anne was irritated as she handed over the phone.

"He wants you."

"Grandad, how many birds are mentioned in the Bible?"

I had to smile. Why didn't he ask Granny? Grandchildren usually turn to Granny; Grandad is just an also-ran!

Christopher explained. He had been handed the questions at school on the Friday afternoon. Answers were to be in on the Monday morning.

I thought I knew my Bible, but how many birds are mentioned?

To start with, Noah sent out a raven, and then a dove, after the flood.

As the people of Israel passed through the desert they complained of no food. The Lord sent meat to eat in the form of quails.

Anne also said that an eagle was mentioned somewhere in the Bible. Sparrows, we both agreed, came up on a number of occasions.

Anne thought the most likely place to find a mention of the odd bird was in the Psalms.

"You take the first fifty and I'll do to a hundred."

The things you do on a Friday night for your eleven-year-old grandchild.

I'd got to about Psalm six when I declared there must be an easier way. Those psalms of David were long!

"Let's ring the minister," Anne suggested. "He'll have one of those Bible dictionaries that tell you everything."

I knew what Anne meant, but I didn't think that would be playing the game. Christopher had asked us for help, not the minister, I pointed out. He could have rung his own in Edinburgh if he'd wanted to. Instead, he'd turned to us.

Anne remarked that I was a sentimental old fool. And I thought her comment about me refusing to try to get help when I didn't know the answer was really scathing.

In a way I see her point. She would have asked that fellow in the sky,

called Gabriel, if she thought he might help Christopher.

"I know; I'll ring Elsie," Anne said suddenly. "She was a Sunday school teacher in my day. She'll know all the answers."

If dear Elsie had been a teacher in Anne's day she wouldn't be any chicken now! I smiled, but said nothing to Anne.

Was chicken mentioned in the Bible? I seemed to recall them being sold in the Temple.

Elsie came up with two we hadn't remembered – stork and heron.

I was just about dropping off to sleep when I got a dig in the back.

"John, we forgot a cock."

I was not pleased.

Next day we wrote out our list – raven, dove, quail, swallow, heron, eagle, cock, pelican, swan, crane and kite.

When we rang Christopher, he was delighted. We'd got four more than his mum and dad!

We rang later in the week to see if any other parents – or grandparents – had remembered more.

Christopher didn't know. All the kids had been told was: "A very good try, boys."

I have my doubts if the teacher had even bothered to make his own list!

Pity – I'd be interested to see how many we missed. ▮

A peaceful spot.

It's A
Gift

Don't Forget To Write

Anne was only in hospital for a week, but I wrote to her every day!

WHAT do you buy your wife as a "coming-out-of-hospital" present? I suppose there must be hundreds of answers to that question, but I was only interested in finding one. My dear Anne had been in hospital for nearly a week, having something done to her eye. It was a long, dreary, lonely week.

You'll probably say I'm a sentimental old man, but I wrote to her every day. They were not long letters, but she told me how much she enjoyed getting them.

I had a routine. Before going across the yard to do the evening milking, I would sit down and tell her what had been happening. All about going up to the top fields, or the birds I'd seen, and the animals.

After milking I'd have my tea – a scratch affair, I'm afraid. Then I'd get changed and set off to the hospital and my Anne. In my pocket was the letter, with a first-class stamp.

It may seem daft to you when I could have given Anne her letter for the next day. But it wasn't daft to me. I took it to the box in the hospital and posted it.

Some postman, after emptying the box, must have taken each letter into the sorting office and then brought it back to the hospital! I don't care. Anne got it – and always thanked me.

When Anne was told she could come back home I suspect she was a wee bit disappointed at leaving her pals. It was a six-bedded ward and they all seemed to get on fine.

She came out with four pieces of paper with names, addresses and telephone numbers.

"Bye, bye, love. Don't forget to give us a ring now!" they shouted as she left that happy ward.

But I still hadn't made up my mind what to give her as a hospital-leaving present . . .

A box of chocolates – no. A bunch of flowers – no. A best leg of lamb – no. I could just hear Anne asking if I was buying it for her or my

own benefit!

Thinking about eating – Anne says I do nothing else – I had wondered what to do. I was to pick her up at about three o'clock in the afternoon and bring her home. Should I take her out somewhere for a high tea? No, she would be tired and want to get back to the Riggin.

I decided to lay on a high tea at home.

I bought two thick, large gammon rashers and cooked them slowly. Then I made a salad of lettuce, tomatoes, four boiled eggs, peppers and spring onions. I served it with a peach on top, as I'd seen in one of Anne's cookery books. Very tasty it was, too.

Back to this hospital-leaving present. I got the answer as I was washing up all the pans I'd used. A bead plant.

Some time back we were at a house in Kingsbarns. The dear lady showed Anne her bead plant collection, which was a real treat.

"I'd love one of those plants," Anne said on our way home.

I jumped into the buggy and tore into St Andrews. I only found one wee bead plant. It looked a poor specimen. I haggled and got two pounds off the price!

When I got home I tried to make it look bigger by putting it on a stand in the middle of the table. Anne was delighted with it.

Unfortunately, not all tales end happily ever after. It died.

I must slip into Kingsbarns and try to persuade the dear lady with lots to sell me one. I'd like Anne to have it to cherish and, I hope, live for years. ■

Present Trends

Anne loves weddings, but she would prefer to choose her own gift for the happy couple . . .

LISTEN, John —"

As soon as our daily newspaper arrives, Anne goes through the engagements, marriages, births and deaths – in that order – and reads them out.

Her day is made if she can then get on the phone!

"Oh, Alice, I was delighted to read your Jim has . . ." Then they will blether on for about half an hour about the young man's engagement.

Invariably I hear, "Alice, what do they want as a present?"

And, these days, the reply is, "Oh, how nice of you, Anne. I'll send the list."

The list will duly arrive. Pages of foolscap with everything you could think of. The first time it happened Anne was really taken aback – and I've put that mildly!

In our day, which I admit wasn't yesterday, there was no such thing as a wedding present list. You gave what you could afford and what you thought might help the young couple make ends meet.

When Anne and I got married, Auntie Mabel and Uncle Jim gave us – would you believe it – a cow in milk!

Anne's young brother gave us six year-old lambs. Her two young sisters gave us a young bullock.

Anne's mother must have spent a fortune. She bought us pots and pans, sieves, cooling trays, a mincer – well, nearly anything needed for the kitchen.

They were all best quality and are still going strong, bless her.

Why, only the other day, Anne and I were changing the bed. She produced two very large linen sheets.

"John and Anne Winder gave us these, remember?" she said. "You can't buy them today."

A woodcarver in the village of Arncroach made our present with his own hands. It was a bread board and carving knife with wooden handle which slid into the side of the board.

Back to these lists. I suppose there is a certain logic to them these days.

I remember our daughter, Mary, bought a beautiful hand-made woven basket for holding logs. As we were going to Edinburgh she asked if we would deliver it to her friend who was to be the bride.

We duly found the house and lugged this beautiful log basket up the garden path.

Mother came to the door, followed by daughter. We explained the basket was from our daughter and that we hoped it would look nice by her fireplace.

"Oh, Mum! I've only got electric fires!" Mary's friend exclaimed.

Anyway, off Anne went to St Andrews with the list.

Her first stop was a china shop. She'd decided on some dishes, oven to table, priced at, I think, £17.

Anne told the assistant they were for a wedding present and mentioned the bride. If she had already got them, could she change them?

The assistant disappeared and came back with the same list Anne had.

"Oh, I'm sorry, Mrs Taylor, she has already got these. They're marked off my list."

Anne was not amused. She thanked the assistant and walked out.

The young couple got a present eventually. A very nice but small Russell Flint print. Not on the list.

We were sitting by the fire that night when Anne said, "I wonder if some day folk will buy wedding presents by pressing a computer button and pay by pressing another?"

We decided we'd still rather have a cow. Or even a wee pig. ▓

Fair Trade

I have "bean" and done it again – and Anne's not happy!

ANNE says I'm odd. That may be so. She has lived with me for over 50 years, so she should know.

But I wonder what she would say if I said, "Anne, you are odd." I can just see her going in a huff and banging whichever door she flounced through!

Well, I may be odd, but I don't like being told, either. Perhaps I'm just odd in, what is to my mind, a very odd world.

For instance, I believe in paying for everything I get . . .

I was in Cupar market when I was joined by Paul, a farmer on the banks of the Tay near Newburgh. His wife, Fiona, and my Anne are pals.

"John, I know you love to eat."

He laughed as he said it. You only have to look at my 18-stone frame to see I enjoy my food!

"Like some runner beans, John? Should slim you down."

I'm a great one for any vegetables, so I said, "Yes, I'd love them."

He walked over to the back of his buggy and brought out a plastic bag full of runner beans. Apparently that morning he had called on one of his men who had worked for him for over 40 years to see how he and his wife were getting on in their retirement.

Jock, the retired farm labourer, had spent his retirement in his large garden. He grew far more than he and his wife could eat. They didn't own a deep freeze, so he gave lots away.

Now I don't like taking anything for nothing. When I got Paul's runner beans and he wouldn't take a penny, I wondered how I could repay him.

If I have to pay back a favour, I usually drop in a small bag of potatoes or a turnip or two. But to take Paul a bag of potatoes would be like taking coals to Newcastle. He grows acres of potatoes!

Anne's very good at thank-you presents. It all depends on who it is, she says.

A pot of marmalade, or perhaps of jam . . . Two lamb chops to some old soul . . . or a piece of pork if we have been killing a pig.

As I sat in the auction ring watching some lambs being sold, I tried to think what Anne would give in return for a bag of runner beans.

I remembered her telling me that when she and a friend came back from a WRI do in Perth, Paul's wife had given them a glass of sherry before sandwiches and coffee. Was that the answer – a bottle of sherry?

I'm not an expert on sherries, so I called in at a wine shop and asked for a good sherry.

Did I want dry or sweet? The assistant then rattled off various names.

I just told them again to give me a good sherry. Later I handed it to Paul as he was getting into his buggy.

"Give that to Fiona, will you? And thanks for the beans."

Well, how was I to know Paul would be home before me?

Fiona had rung my Anne to say thank you for the bottle of sherry I had sent her.

Yes, you can guess, I got a cold reception. Even when I explained why I had sent the sherry, I was still in the wrong. Fiona had got the best of the bargain – the beans, to hear Anne talk, were not worth more than a few pence!

You can't win, can you? ▥

A Prickly Problem

Find a hedgehog for a friend?
Anne has set me a mission implausible!

THE phone rang on Friday, at twelve-fifteen. We were in the middle of one of Anne's mouth-watering lunches. She'd cooked a leg of lamb and we were just starting the main course, with roast potatoes, brussels sprouts and home-made mint sauce.

If I'd picked it up, I would have said, "Sorry, she's out. I'll get her to ring you when she comes back."

But it was Anne herself who answered. She chatted and giggled like a schoolgirl as she and the caller discussed their last game of bridge.

I didn't see any sense in being a gentleman and waiting till Anne had finished her idle chatter. I put her plate in the oven and went on eating.

"Bye, bye, Olive," she said eventually. "I'm sure John will find one."

I recovered her plate and put it before her.

"That was Olive."

As if I didn't know!

"Her Niall's birthday is next Friday. She wants to give him a hedgehog. I said you'd get her one."

Now how did a woman come up with the idea of giving her husband a hedgehog as a birthday present?

Apparently Olive had heard Niall say that if they only had a hedgehog, they would have no slugs in the garden!

Hence the idea . . . hence the phone call . . . hence Anne's answer, "I'm sure John will find one."

Normally I would have said, "Nae bother," but then I began to think about it. And I realised how long it had been since Jip last growled at a rolled-up ball of spikes. Oh, I'd seen lots of the poor things dead on the road, but there certainly aren't as many on the Riggin as there used to be.

Still, I had a week to produce the goods.

I usually take the tractor when I look over the stock of sheep on our top land, but I started to walk instead – Anne said it was good for me – to try to find that wee, spiky fellow. But even Jip, after being told what

I wanted, couldn't find one.

As the days passed, I began to dread another phone call from Olive to find out how I was getting on. I even half-expected her to ring to ask if I would get her a pair so that they would breed for her dear Niall!

That thought made me chuckle, as I haven't the slightest idea how to tell a male from a female hedgehog!

By Tuesday I hadn't even caught one hedgehog – male or female – and I was getting desperate.

After all, I have a certain pride. If my Anne said, "John will find one", I wasn't going to let her down.

That evening I jumped in the buggy and went to see an old friend of mine. Alister is a keeper on one of the estates near Colinsburgh.

"Nae bother, John," he said happily when I told him my problem.

Off we set, accompanied by his two gun dogs, who were happy to be released from the kennels.

Within ten minutes a hedgehog had been located and popped into his game bag. I didn't ask if it was male or female!

Anne never did know where Niall's present came from. She just delivered the prickly object on the Thursday evening.

Within a week it had found that there was greener grass – or bigger slugs – in someone else's garden! ▪

Springtime in the fields.

A Bargain Buy

When I decided to buy some bargain fruit, I found myself in a real jam!

ANNE loves raspberries, but I'm afraid I don't share her joy for these red berries full of little hard seeds. They always seem to get stuck between my teeth.

It was early July and I was walking up South Street, St Andrews, from the port, and passed a greengrocer's. On the stand outside the shop window were about 10 punnets of large rasps. The label said, *Local dessert rasps – 60 pence per punnet*.

I asked the assistant to keep aside a punnet for me until I came back from seeing the accountant.

As I came out of the greengrocer's, I saw the dairy opposite and decided to go across and buy one of their cartons of double cream. This I deposited with the lassie looking after my dessert rasps.

The accountant painted a gloomy picture of our farming activities and made me wish I hadn't bought the rasps or the cream.

About a month later I found myself buying rasps again. It was the last Saturday in August and for some reason, I can't now remember why, I'd gone into Cupar.

I parked the car in the big car park in Bonnygate and was walking towards Cupar Cross when I passed another greengrocer's. There was a sign outside advertising rasps at 30p per pound.

I went into the shop and told the lassie to put aside six pounds and I'd collect them later.

"They're jamming rasps," she told me. "They're not really suitable for eating."

It was very good of her to be honest, I thought, but I decided I'd have them anyway.

As I was coming back from seeing the miller I remembered the lassie had said they were jamming rasps. Now, even I know you need sugar to make jam. I asked the lassie in the fruit shop how much sugar I'd need for six pounds of rasps. Unfortunately she hadn't a clue and said that she never made jam.

Fortunately a woman customer said, "It's a pound a pound. I know, I've just made some myself."

So I had to buy six pounds of sugar. My bargain was beginning to look like less of a bargain.

After arriving back home I put my bargain rasps on the draining board as I'd seen they were beginning to seep out of the bag.

Anne took one look.

"Who gave you those?" she asked.

"I bought them; they were going cheap, thirty pence a pound."

"John Taylor, those won't keep till tomorrow. I'll have to make them into jam tonight and I doubt if I've enough sugar."

"I've bought sugar, dear," I told her with a superior air.

"I bet the woman who sold you these said they were jamming rasps and had to be jammed today," she went on.

"She did say they were jamming rasps, but said nothing about them having to be done today."

"Of course she wouldn't. There aren't many wives who are daft enough to make jam on a Saturday night."

I didn't ask what they'd be doing instead as Anne would have said they'd be with their husbands enjoying a Saturday night out.

The jam pan came out and was buttered on side and bottom. The jam was duly boiled and jars were found and washed.

The scum was removed and after it came to the boil it was boiled hard for 15 minutes. Anne had to admit it smelled delicious.

After that Anne poured the jam into jars while I covered and labelled them.

Well, I hope Anne enjoys it. As I said before, raspberries are not my favourite fruit. I began to wonder why on earth I'd bought them, but as Anne says, I can't pass a bargain. It seems she's right – as usual! ▨

A Stitch In Time

Call me an old sew-and-sew, but there are some things I like to do for myself!

THERE are certain things a man likes to do on his own. And to my mind, that includes shopping for certain items of clothing.

My daughter has refused to go shopping with her old man. She says I ask ridiculous questions. Well, when I'm paying, why not?

I wanted a new pair of braces. They had to be long and strong and fit on to buttons. The clip type are hopeless.

I went into the men's shop in Cupar. A laddie brought out a selection of braces.

They were all in decorative boxes with see-through fronts. Why? You have to pay for the packaging – and then it goes in the dustbin when you get home!

"Extra large, sir?" the laddie asked me.

I nodded and told him I wanted to try them on.

He looked worried. If he took them out of the box and I didn't buy, would he be able to put them back again?

He looked across at the owner of the shop to see what he should do. The boss smiled and nodded his head. John and Anne Taylor, plus parents on both sides, have shopped there for years!

The laddie carefully extracted the braces. He handed them to me and I threw them over my shoulders. Then, to his obvious surprise, I said, "Now you fasten the back. I'll do the front."

New braces are very stiff and I wasn't going to stand there struggling. They fitted. I paid.

"Shall I wrap them up, sir?"

I handed him my old braces to put in a paper bag and kept the new ones on!

While I was waiting I saw a farm-worker's large wife come in with her wee husband. She completely overpowered him. He didn't say a word while she did his shopping for him. She ended up telling him so loudly the whole shop could hear, "Man, you're hopeless. You can't buy yourself a pair of socks."

My heart bled for the poor wee chap. How I wished I could help that poor, downtrodden man. I could have said as I left, "Madam, have you ever given your husband the chance to buy anything for himself?" But I didn't. I was too flabbergasted.

The other night I was "caught" myself!

I told Anne I was going up to my wee room to write and tell you what was happening on the Riggin. I really went up to do some vital running repairs.

That morning I had bent down getting out of bed. Ping! I knew the button that held my pyjama trousers up against the law of gravity had decided it could no longer take the strain.

I deliberately didn't say anything to Anne because I knew I would be given a lecture about my weight. And probably put on a diet . . .

I was busily sewing when her ladyship poked her nose round the door.

"John, I would have done that if you asked."

So she would have done – but I couldn't ask her. And I didn't want her to see I wasn't just sewing the button on. I was giving it a "tail". I reckoned an extra inch would come in useful next time I bent down!

When it comes to pyjamas, I'm a bit like that wee man in Cupar. I'm never allowed to choose them myself. I suppose I should be grateful I'm given them as presents.

If Anne and our daughter would only let me buy my own . . . I'd go around all the shops to find a good old-fashioned one which still sold pyjamas with cords. Cords are adjustable and can't go "ping".

The last time Anne and my daughter asked me what I wanted for my birthday, I surprised them by not saying, "Whatever you want to give me." I didn't want any more shirts or socks – or pyjamas – did I?

"A silk tie, please," I answered instead.

I got two beauties! Aren't I a lucky man?

An Apple A Day

. . . can be too much of a good thing, as I soon found out.

ANNE'S having a jolly good laugh at me – she's grinning from ear to ear, like a Cheshire cat.

I had gone into Cupar on the Thursday to the store sale as we wanted 10 bullocks.

I walked up the street and looked in a fruit shop. Anne says I always make a bee-line for any shop that sells anything edible. That's not true, but I did stop outside that greengrocer's. I saw cauliflowers were reduced in price. Now Anne does a cauliflower in a cream cheese sauce which melts in the mouth. She did it last week and topped it with a poached egg.

I thought I would buy her a cauliflower. I picked up one of those wire baskets. A fatal move – I always end up trying to fill it.

Well, I saw Victoria plums – lovely, ripe ones. Seeing those plums took me back to the time Dad and I were left on our own when Mother went for a two-week holiday in the south of England.

We had plum trees full and we – Dad and I – seemed to have plums and custard at every meal. Dad was adept at making instant custard.

Well, I bought some onions, carrots and celery and put them in my basket. Just as I got to where the girl weighs your bits, and their plastic bags, I noticed a big box, half full of apples.

They had been rejected for sale but they looked all right to me. I asked an assistant what they would take for the apples. The manageress came and I repeated my request.

She named a price I considered extremely reasonable and I agreed to buy.

For once I had kept my big mouth shut and waited. I usually say, "I'll give you such-and-such for that." In this case, I would have offered double what she charged me. What a bargain!

Was it? I'm not so sure now as I write these notes at a quarter past eleven at night. Anne's in bed.

It was obvious that if I didn't deal with those darned apples after supper, some would only be fit for the pig.

Well, at least if the pig got them, they wouldn't be wasted.

I set off to peel them. Anne offered to help, in a very half-hearted way, when she had done the ironing.

I peeled and peeled and peeled again. I filled the jam pan with apples. I filled two other large pans with apples and finally left a quarter of the apples in the box unpeeled. If they go bad by tomorrow night, I'm sure the pig will enjoy them.

Anne, who is a practical sort, then asked a difficult question.

"John, what are you going to do with all those apples?"

I thought quickly. What was I going to do with them?

"Well, dear, you can make apple-pies, have them with pork or have apple and ice-cream for a pudding."

"You mean 'sweet', John."

I'm old-fashioned.

"We can give some to the children."

That's our son and daughter, both of whom have families.

"John, if you had waited, they'd both have brought you a sack of fallen apples."

They both have orchards with apple trees.

My bargain wasn't being received with open arms.

Well, they all went, after more peeling, into plastic containers and then into the deep freeze.

When they will be used I don't know, but I still maintain they were a bargain. ◾

Going, Going, Gone

There was something I wanted to buy, but Anne soon put paid to my auction bidding!

"S IR – the gentleman in the fifth row – the bidding is against you at six hundred pounds."

All of a sudden Anne woke up to the fact that I was the gentleman in the fifth row!

"Have you gone out of your mind? Stop bidding!"

The next bid went to £650. I did as I was told and dropped out. I'll never forgive myself.

I wonder what he, or she – I couldn't see who was bidding against me – would have gone up to before calling it a day?

It only needs two farmers who both decide they must have a prize bull to send the price up and up.

I would have gone on – oh, no, not for a bull – but for a certain stool which came under the auctioneer's hammer at Earlshall, in Fife, one day a few years ago.

Anne wanted to go to the viewing of the sale and asked me to go with her. Like her, I enjoy looking at beautiful furniture.

There were over 1,000 lots for sale and half of Scotland seemed to be there to view them. Anne marked item 76 in the catalogue – an inlaid games board.

"The boys would love it," she said. "I'll buy it if the price is reasonable. Will you come back with me on Monday, John?"

I agreed. I wanted to go anyway. I had marked item 46 down for my most careful attention.

It was an oak joint stool, with moulded rectangular top and moulded frieze on turned baluster legs and square stretchers. Seventeenth century. Eighteen inches wide.

I made certain, as we left the farm, that I had my cheque book.

"Now, John, you won't get carried away and bid for anything, will you?" Anne warned as we cruised into St Andrews.

I never uttered a word.

As we parked the car we saw a big tent, like a circus marquee, had been erected on the lawn. The sale was in the tent.

As we entered, a lady handed us a wooden paddle-like thing with a number on it. She put our name against the number in her book.

"Just hold that up when you have bought anything," the lady explained.

"John, we're not buying anything. Why did you take that thing?"

"Just in case you get your games board," I told her. Really, I hoped to raise it high, having been the last bidder for item 46.

Why was I so keen on buying that stool?

Well, long ago, I didn't know what to give Anne for her twenty-first birthday. Eventually I saw an oak stool in a shop in Dirleton, a village in East Lothian, and decided that was the answer to my problem.

I cycled all the way back from Dirleton, down to the ferry at South Queensferry and right through Fife to the Riggin, with that stool on my back. It wasn't an antique then, but Anne thought it was beautiful.

The stool at Earlshall was definitely an antique – and identical to the one I'd bought in Dirleton.

I suppose it was just as well I didn't get it. It would have created a big problem that Solomon with all his wisdom could not have solved. Should our son, Paul, have the "twenty-first" stool, with all its associations and love? And should our daughter, Mary, have the genuine antique one, worth well over £600?

Now the only problem will be – who will claim Anne's twenty-first birthday present? ▦

Heads You Win

I can never resist a bargain, even if it does vex Anne!

I NEVER quite know what to buy at our church "dos".
We seem to have them more often nowadays and it's incredible
what they raise in cash. Just last Sunday, the minister told us that the
latest Women's Guild coffee morning raised the magnificent sum of
£1,230!

Usually at sales of work, I leave Anne and head for the food. I really
enjoy the cake and vegetables stalls!

At the last do I found myself wandering past the "bits and pieces"
stall. You know the sort of thing – people don't want something or
other any longer, but can't bring themselves to put it in the dustbin –
so they send it to the church sale!

I saw a large headsquare in yellow with horse heads in black. It was
crushed, but an iron would sort that out, I decided, so I bought it.

I also bought four linen – real Irish linen – napkins. They were
oatmeal in colour and someone had embroidered a bunch of forget-
me-nots in one corner of each one. They were really pretty.

When we got back to the Riggin, I put my bargains on the kitchen
table. Anne thought I'd bought them for her. She picked up the
headsquare.

"I'll wear it at the Balcormo races."

I had to smile. Anne has so many headsquares she didn't need
another. I hadn't bought it for her . . .

She picked up the napkins.

"Why didn't you buy six?"

Can't women be awkward? Or is it that they just don't think?

If there had been six, I would have bought them. Or eight, for that
matter. There were only four on offer.

"Why did you buy them?"

When I told her it was for our only granddaughter, Anne's face fell.
She is the apple of our eye. We have three grandsons, but only one
granddaughter.

"Oh, John, what does she want with linen napkins?"

"I thought she could put them in her bottom drawer."

Anne gave me one of her looks.

Don't girls have bottom drawers these days?

I know my Anne had. She made pillowcases, hand towels with embroidered corners, knitted dish cloths and all manner of little things for her home when she had one.

One of the favourite things for a bottom drawer was a pegged rug. Whenever a couple got engaged everyone set to and made a rag rug to use in front of the fire.

Looking back, Anne says these were real dust-catchers. It took two to give it a good shake.

A few weeks after the sale, Anne happened to be in St Andrews and she parked the farm buggy beside a china shop.

The huge notice in the window said, *25% off all goods*.

Like me, Anne can't resist a bargain. She came back with a really beautiful tea service.

"Darling, do we really need it at our age?" I asked as she spread it out on the kitchen table.

Another of Anne's withering looks followed.

"It's for the first grandchild who gets married."

If that isn't for someone's bottom drawer, I don't know what is!

Oh, I forgot to tell you. Our granddaughter thanked me nicely for the headsquare and napkins. She even gave me a peck on the cheek. That made my day! ▰

Suit You, Sir

Anne's encounter with a smart salesman left me out of pocket!

'VE never been one for buying clothes. I've always had a Sunday suit for church, but after that I couldn't care less, much, I must say, to Anne's dismay.

To hear my Anne speak, you'd think I was the worst-dressed man in the East Neuk of Fife.

The lecture on trying, at least, to look respectable came about after one of those pinstripe-suited salesmen had called at the farm.

I was out, thank goodness, but Anne certainly made sure she told me everything about him I needed to know.

He'd driven into the yard, opened the rear door of his car then taken his jacket off a coat-hanger. He gave it a little shake, put it on and proceeded to our back door.

How long Anne talked to this tailor's dummy, I'll never know. Did she give him tea and scones? I didn't ask.

After leaving Anne, he'd reversed the process. The jacket was removed and placed back on the hanger before driving off with a wave to Anne.

Over lunch she asked me why I didn't take my jacket off when I got in the car.

I ask you! I had to laugh, much to Anne's annoyance.

Well, I only wear my good suit for weddings and funerals and church. As it takes us only five minutes from the farm to Kingsbarns Church, I'm not, for Anne's sake nor anybody else's, going to put my jacket on a hanger for the journey. It's not on me long enough to gather any wrinkles!

I was taken to Dundee recently. Anne had promised one of our grandsons a suit as a birthday present.

He phoned her to tell her what he'd seen.

"I've chosen a suit, Gran," he said. "But I've left it for you to look at to see if you like it, too."

Without more ado, Anne arranged that she and I should go to Dundee next day to look at the suit.

I soon realised I should have stayed in the car and let her go to examine the suit herself.

Oh, yes, she approved of our grandson's choice – but then she turned her attentions elsewhere.

"Have you a suit that will fit him?" she asked.

"Him" was little me.

The assistant struggled to put a tape measure round my waist. He looked at the outcome and was most polite.

"Perhaps sir would care to go down to the basement where they have suits for larger gentlemen."

Anne knows I'm not one for dressing up, but we came out of that shop with a suit, a sports jacket, a pair of flannel trousers and two pairs of socks.

I told you, I should have stayed in the car.

I've seen the day when I'd have taken Anne out to high tea if we happened to be in Dundee, but there was no high tea that day after wasting so much time and money on clothes.

It's all a waste of time if you ask me.

I'm much happier dressed in my old trousers and shirt with my old knitted woolly bonnet – although every time I put that on, Anne seems to frown.

If you ask me, clothes are to keep the cold out, and mine do the job. I might not be stylish, but at least I'm warm. ▮

To Cap It All

Sometimes I have trouble keeping abreast of my bunnet!

THE best headgear to wear on our Riggin fields is really a woolly hat that you can just pull on your head and over your ears like a tea-cosy.

I put one on, but dear Anne objected strongly. She insisted I wear a cap.

I'm never one for having half a dozen of any piece of clothing. Some men seem to have endless changes.

The only thing I have in abundance is pyjamas. I've four pairs. You may think that's really extravagant, and I would agree. But not my dear Anne.

"If you have to go into hospital, you'll need changes," she informed me.

I hope I don't have to go into hospital, but Anne's motto, like the Girl Guides, is "be prepared."

We've had them in the hospital drawer for so long that I doubt the trousers will go round me any more.

When I was a boy, your pyjama trousers were fastened with a cord. And if you lost the cord, you had to borrow a hair-grip or a safety-pin to thread it through again. Nowadays they have elasticated waists and even a button!

But I've got sidetracked again. I was telling you about my cap.

I had one I liked that fitted real snug, but had gone a bit out of shape at the front. Anne said it made me look like Norman Wisdom!

The outcome was that Anne gave me a cap at Christmas.

By the way, caps are not the five-shilling price they were when I was a boy.

I remember another occasion when Anne told me that I needed a new cap.

Not long after she said that, I had business in St Andrews, so while I was there I decided to treat myself and I went into a rather posh men's outfitters.

I chose a cap, gave the laddie a five-pound note and waited for the change.

In the end I had to ask him for it.

"But it was five pounds exactly, sir," he told me with a surprised look.

If I hadn't already put it on my head, I'd have told him to keep it.

Well, before Christmas, Anne and I went to buy me a new cap.

I noticed she didn't go to the posh shop, but to a more traditional one.

We tried on lots and eventually got one not only to fit, but which didn't look too pouched or floppy.

The reason I'm telling you about my cap is because I've lost it. I'd been looking for it for days off and on, but I hadn't told Anne.

In the end I had to pluck up the courage to say, "Anne, have you seen my new cap?"

"John, have you lost it?" she asked as quick as a flash.

"No, dear, I've just misplaced it. I thought you might have put it away until I went into hospital."

That, I may say, didn't go down at all well.

"Let's think – where have you been in the last week?"

I'd been to the barber's to have my hair cut, as well as half a dozen other places.

I went to visit each one and explained about my lost Christmas present. Everyone was very sympathetic, but no cap.

In the end, I went to the St Andrews police station.

"Sorry, sir," I was told sympathetically. "We can't help you there."

Now Anne's branded me as being hopeless, so I hope it pops up somewhere in the house.

Hope, with me, springs eternal, but I think even hope in this case is rather thin.

But at least there's one consolation. If it doesn't turn up, Anne knows what to buy me for next Christmas! ▦

What Am I Bid?

The old tray is battered and grubby, but no amount of money could buy it from us now . . .

"**S**HALL I throw it out?"

Anne held up a tray which had seen better days.

I didn't hesitate.

"Don't you dare!"

It was an oval tray, the centre adorned with a picture of a robin and basket work round the edge. We've used it non-stop for 40 years at least.

"John, look at it! It's a mess!"

I did, and Anne was right – it was. It was bashed and stained and it certainly reflected its long and useful life.

But although its value in money terms might have been little or nothing, in sentimental terms, to me it was worth a million pounds.

When Anne and I were young, all the church social activities were held in the upper room above the church stables.

It wasn't ideal – it was draughty, not the most comfortable, and probably a bit of a fire hazard – and eventually we started fund-raising for a new hall.

One event was an auction of farm animals and other gifts. One farmer gave a cow, another two sheep and so on.

The sale was held in a field next to the church. Luckily it was a nice day. I remember being amazed when I saw one top-class calf coming into the ring.

Some generous soul must have given their best young beast for the sale.

Well, four different farmers bought that calf and put it straight back into the sale.

Then a young man who had just started farming entered the bidding and everyone else dropped out. In a matter of minutes the calf was his.

Anne bid for four eight-week-old piglets and got them. She paid over the odds, but I wasn't worried – I knew she would make them earn their keep and show a profit.

I had no intention of bidding for anything until the tray came up, and Anne nudged me.

"Bid for that, John. We need a tray."

After some brisk bidding, and some jocular conversation across the ring, it was knocked down to me.

"Anne will be getting her breakfast in bed on that!" the auctioneer called, and everyone laughed.

When the laughter had subsided, a wee lassie of about twelve came running round the ring and threw her arms round Anne.

"Oh, Mrs Taylor, I'm so glad you bought that tray, because it's one that I made!"

She had been in Anne's Sunday school class and they obviously still had a great deal of affection for each other. It's times like that I feel very proud of my Anne.

We farmers get a name for being hard, but on occasions like that sale, when we get together to support a worthy cause, we can show our softer side.

If a young farmer's wife loses her husband and has to sell up, we will rally round at the farm sale.

The prices paid for beasts and machinery usually well exceed their true value. We all want to help in times of trouble and to us that is a practical and unobtrusive way to do it.

And I, for one, wouldn't have it any other way . . . ▓

When Is A Bargain Not A Bargain?

When, as I found to my cost, there are hidden extras to pay!

I WAS nineteen when I went with some friends to visit a farm in the Vale of York. We went by bus and stayed overnight in York. When I got back, I could talk of nothing else, according to Anne, so I always promised that I would take her there one day.

Some years later, we managed a trip to the Great Yorkshire Show. On the way, we stopped for a break in that delightful wee town of Corbridge.

We decided to have lunch at the inn, which looks down on to the old stone bridge over the Tyne. I parked the car in the main street, just outside a butcher's shop.

"Trust you," Anne said, "to park outside a butcher's."

Looking in the window, we were impressed by the display and how clean everything looked. Not only that, but the prices were cheaper than back home, too.

"That's a nice lamb, John," Anne commented.

On impulse, we went in. We asked the price of the lamb in the window and if the butcher would cut it up for the freezer.

We decided that we would call in and collect it on our way north the following Thursday afternoon. That was when we hit a snag – he was closed on Thursday afternoons.

"I'll leave the yard door on the latch and you can pick it up. It'll be in a box," he told us.

We wanted to pay in advance, but he wouldn't hear of it. He would leave the bill on top of the box and we could put a cheque through the door. The kindness and trust of that butcher is something I'll always remember.

My next venture into bulk buying also went well, but led me into real trouble with Anne.

We had gone to stay for a few days with a relative of Anne's near Kirkby Lonsdale.

While the ladies went sightseeing in Lancaster, Tom and I had a stroll through the covered market.

We soon came across a pork butcher's shop. It was the kind of shop we don't have in Fife. I'm told they use every part of the pig and even bottle the grunt!

I wandered in and gave an order for pork pies, proper black puddings, bacon, chops and joints of pork. As we were leaving for home the next day, I arranged to pick it up in the morning.

Eventually, all those black puddings were finished and there were no pies left for a late-night snack.

I got out the bill and decided to place the same order again. My only problem would be getting the goods to Fife.

I rang Leuchars station. Yes, a weekday train ran from Lancaster around four o'clock, arriving in Leuchars four hours later.

I posted my order to Lancaster and asked them to put the parcel on the train the following Thursday.

"Did you ask how much it would cost to send?" Anne asked.

I hadn't. There and then, Anne rang the station and asked the price. When she told me, I almost passed out.

Unfortunately, it was too late – the order was in.

Well, I daren't tell you what I paid for that delivery, but I'll never do it again. I must have paid for half the engine that pulled the train.

I always say, you live and learn.

Anne disagrees with that statement. She says I'll never learn! ■

Anne's scones are out of this world!

Out And About

A Day To Remember

That was one visit to the Perth bull sales that I wouldn't forget in a hurry!

WE all make mistakes. Perhaps I had better say that some of us do, in case you are one of those fortunate persons who has never made a mistake.

Anne says I will never learn. Sometimes I'm forced to agree with her.

Anne had read in our local paper that the bull sales were on in Perth and she suggested that we went. I had some reservations – the Perth bull sales are not really for dirty-boot farmers like yours truly, but more for landed gentry.

Still, if Anne wanted to go, I was game to take her. Like a couple of youngsters – which we certainly aren't – we got up at half-past five in the morning to get through our various tasks.

Thank goodness we now have electricity in all the buildings. We used to have to go round with a paraffin lantern.

Anne came to help with the milking, but the cows weren't anxious to let down their milk; they obviously objected to having their beauty sleep interrupted.

Anne went to make breakfast while I swept out the byre.

I entered the kitchen and there was an aroma that made me feel it was good to be alive. Anne had decided, as we might not get much lunch, that we should have a good breakfast. It was the kind I'm not supposed to eat: porridge followed by lashings of bacon, two eggs and a thick slice of fried bread, washed down with a mug of coffee.

I did the dishes while Anne went to get "dolled up". If she was going to the famous Perth bull sales, she wasn't going to let me down.

I was proud of her. She wore a beautiful fur hat, an oatmeal and green coat and her long boots.

We set off just before eight o'clock, but had to watch our speed. A sudden frost had come down and the roads were very slippy indeed.

Well, we arrived in Perth all in one piece and had a memorable day. Anne had half an eye on the beasts going through the ring and half an eye on what the other wives were wearing.

At lunchtime we had an open sandwich and a coffee at a nearby hotel. There were a number of other bull buyers' wives there and Anne enjoyed herself immensely.

We went into an antiques shop just to look around and Anne picked up a copper fish pan with two copper handles. It was almost black.

Anne asked the price and put it down.

"Not likely," she told the dealer.

However, I could see she liked it, so I offered a price.

"No – that's less than I paid for it," the dealer told me indignantly.

We kept looking round his showrooms, but Anne came back to the copper fish pan. The antiques dealer came away with a figure for cash.

I had been meaning to take Anne out for a dinner to celebrate a very enjoyable day, but if I bought that copper fish pan it meant I couldn't afford it!

We came home, had some of Anne's home-made broth and two pork chops with apple. It was, Anne said, far better than going out.

As soon as that was over, Anne got out the metal polish and rags whilst I washed up. Well, she rubbed and rubbed. I'm told that if it's wet tomorrow, I've to rub with a rag and polish till it shines like a new pin.

As I said, we all make mistakes. If we hadn't gone into that antiques shop "just to look around", Anne wouldn't have seen that fish pan and I wouldn't be faced with the prospect of polishing it. Let's hope it's a fine day tomorrow! ▉

An Evening Out

We shall go to the ball!

FERGUS, are you going to the Farm Mech Ball?" I asked my old friend when I met him one day.

"Not thought about it, John," he told me. "We gave it a miss last year and did I hear about it – Morag said every other farmer and his wife would be there except us."

I told Fergus there were two of us in the same boat. Anne has been preaching that we don't get out enough. She says that if we don't make an effort to socialise, we'll get stuck in a rut.

Anne used to go here and there in her wee car to play bridge at various farms, but not now. I'm to blame, she says. If only I'd learned to play bridge she could have invited them over for bridge parties.

I couldn't think of anything I'd hate more.

I came to an agreement with Fergus. He'd ask Morag to ring my Anne and invite us – as their guests – to the Farm Mech Ball.

"Give Anne the idea you're paying, but don't worry, I'll pay for us, of course," I told him.

Anne fell for Morag's call, hook, line and sinker.

I came in at lunchtime next day.

"John, you'll never guess," she cried. "Morag has been on the phone. "She and Fergus want us to be their guests at the Farm Mech Ball."

"I suppose you politely turned the invitation down," I said solemnly, trying to suppress a smile. "After all, it's a long-dress do, and you haven't one, and besides, I can't get into my penguin suit any more."

Anne gave me one of her looks.

"I've said yes," she told me firmly. "It'll do us good to get out."

I smiled to myself, secretly delighted my ploy had worked.

I was a bit worried, though. After all, it was years since I'd worn my penguin suit and I've really put on the beef since then.

One day when Anne was out I tried the trousers on.

Oh, who mentioned the Farm Mech Ball? By drawing in my tummy, I could get them to meet, but the pain . . .

I couldn't go a whole night like that. In any case, when I eased myself into the driving seat, every button would give up trying to hold me in.

I put them in a bag and threw them into the car. Then I drove – so I told Anne – to see to some business in St Andrews. In fact, I went to a dry-cleaning firm I knew would put a gusset in my trousers.

I didn't dare tell Anne I'd outgrown my suit, otherwise she'd have fed me on bread and water till the ball to get my weight down.

It was three weeks to the ball, but, oh, how I suffered.

"What shall I wear?" Anne kept asking every evening as she rummaged through her wardrobe trying on everything in sight.

Night after night this went on.

"John, does this go with this?"

She'd stand in the doorway wearing a skirt and top – lots of skirts and tops.

I raised my eyes to the heavens. Do people really bother so much about what others are wearing? I don't think so, but my Anne and, I bet, thousands of other wives do.

Well, I'm pleased to say that the dry-cleaning firm put in a three-inch gusset. At least I could breathe.

"John, these trousers have kept their crease really well," Anne observed in surprise.

I agreed. Well, they wouldn't put in the gusset without first dry-cleaning and pressing, but don't tell Anne that.

Morag and Fergus picked us up as our hosts to the ball. Anne looked smashing in a top and long skirt in what she called shot silk.

We crawled into bed just after two.

"We must do it more often, John," Anne said sleepily.

"Why?" was my last word before dropping off. Somehow I didn't think I'd be able to face another trying-on-clothes session for a long time. ▥

Curry Favour

I'm getting all hot and bothered about a new ingredient.

W E – that's Anne and I – were invited out to supper by a fellow farmer and his wife. We read through the menu.

The dearest item was a T-bone steak. If I'd been paying, I would have loved it, but thought I had better go for a middle-of-the road price.

The answer was soup of the day (a thick vegetable soup), followed by curried chicken and coffee.

I well remember in our early days when we weren't so used to eating out, I saw "consomme" on the menu. I asked Anne what it was. She didn't tell me, but suggested I order it. She was sure I'd enjoy it.

I couldn't believe my eyes when it arrived. It wasn't soup, or at least, not my kind of soup. You could see right through to the pattern on the bottom of the plate!

That's the first time I had consomme and the last. It's not for John Taylor. I like body in my soup.

Anyway, Anne chose the curried chicken, but cut out the soup.

As soon as the fellow who took the order had left, she had a go at me.

"John, you shouldn't have ordered the soup at your weight."

Well, I had, and I enjoyed every mouthful. Then came the chicken.

The girl serving me handed me a knife and fork, but I had asked for a spoon. An old friend, who had spent a long time in India, advised me on that. Those in the know always eat curry with a spoon.

When the young lady put the curried chicken in front of Anne and me, it was covered with a pancake kind of thing, so thin that if there had been a draught it would have floated away.

Anne gave me a look. I could see the question in her eyes – what was it and how did you attack it?

David, our host, must have seen, too, and looked at me.

"John, do you know what that is?"

He knew I hadn't a clue.

"It's Bombay Duck."

Was he pulling my leg?

I looked at that flat thing sitting on my curry. If it had ever been a duck swimming about Bombay, it had been grossly underfed!

When we got back to the Riggin that night, Anne went to our old

Pears Dictionary – cost 2/6d.

"A small Indian fish of a family akin to the salmon," she read.

Never!

That lifeless thing on my plate was in no way akin to the Tay salmon.

"Look, we'll buy some curry powder and I'll make you a proper curry from my new recipe book," Anne said.

Where did you get curry powder? I had no idea. Neither did Anne.

I was going through St Andrews on Tuesday and tried to think. The delicatessen in Market Street might have it. I went in and asked.

"Sure, John – here, take that to Anne."

Hot madras curry powder, 100 grams. That sounded just the thing.

Well, I've often told you Anne's trying to get my weight down. So, at teatime (last meal of the day; suppers are now a thing of the past) we would have curried rice and a poached egg in the middle.

How much curry should you add to the rice? Anne added two heaped teaspoonfuls.

We have never laughed so much. Oh, yes, that curried rice was too darned hot! The egg was beautiful and the rice would have been, with a little less hot madras curry powder.

We both cleaned our plates, though, and had a cup of iced tea! It's certainly a meal we'll always remember! ▩

Early Days

Punctuality sometimes leads
me to get ahead of myself . . .

KNOW I have a failing. I also know what Anne will say when she reads this.

"Only one? You must be joking!"

I don't even look at it as a failing – but Anne gets really annoyed with me about it.

When we were courting, if I agreed to meet her outside Edler's Café at twelve noon on a Tuesday, I would be there at five to, not five past the hour. To this day I still break my neck to be there on time.

I hate people who say they will see you at a certain place at a certain time and, without so much as an apology, turn up half an hour late. To me that is the height of bad manners. In fact, I have been known to be rude to farmers who stop me for a blether when I'm rushing to meet Anne.

If a train leaves the station at ten in the morning, it's no good blaming the railway company if you arrive at ten past ten and miss it, is it? To be on the safe side, I would be there at ten minutes to ten.

Whenever Anne and I were going to something, like the theatre, which has a definite starting time, we would be there with time to spare.

When we went to Pitlochry Theatre as a birthday treat for Anne, I wasn't certain how long it would take. Then there was always the chance we might have a puncture . . .

I allowed myself two hours.

Thanks to the bypass at Perth, we arrived with three-quarters of an hour to spare.

We went and sat in the foyer. We hadn't been there more than a couple of minutes when Anne nudged me.

"Oh, look." Then, "Hello, Joan."

Before we went in to see the show, Anne had had a chat with Joan and her husband, plus half a dozen people she knew.

And did I get a "Thank you, John, for being early"? No, I did not!

Of course, even I will admit that you can be too early.

If I told the story of Anne's hospital appointment to my doctor, all he would say would be, "Anno Domini, John." And the annoying thing is that he would be right; I am getting on, and it was all my fault.

Anne got a card from our local hospital in Dundee, asking her to attend the outpatients' department about her eye. We were due at twelve noon.

Now, twelve noon was an awkward time. I knew I'd have to allow for roadworks on the Tay Bridge which would cause delays. Then I might get a puncture . . . and what about the difficulties in parking? We'd better leave at half past ten – too early for lunch.

"Let's have a picnic on the way back," Anne suggested.

I thought it was a good idea. We made some sandwiches of lettuce, tomatoes and cheese, took a packet of biscuits and two bananas. Then there was the flask of hot water, plus the coffee jar. (We found out later I'd forgotten to pack the milk, so we had to have black coffee.)

Despite all my calculations, we arrived at the hospital car park with only seven minutes to spare. We hurried over to the eye clinic and handed the card over.

The lady searched through the files. No Anne Taylor. Then she looked at our appointment card. She was so sweet.

"I'm so sorry, but your appointment is for tomorrow."

Ouch! ▓

Lost And Found

It was no picnic when Anne found a bedraggled teddy bear . . .

ANNE refuses to go to church unless she's wearing a hat and gloves. And I hate being late.

When she was fluttering about last Sunday morning looking for her gloves, I nearly lost my temper.

We made it – without gloves – just as the minister was reading out the church notices for the coming weeks. At least we'd got in before the first hymn.

I don't think Anne took the sermon in. I've lived long enough with her to know she would be wondering where she could have left her gloves.

Could they be in the gutter somewhere, having dropped off her knees as she got out of the car?

As we left the church, she didn't say to the minister, "I enjoyed your sermon", as she usually does. Which confirmed she hadn't a clue what it had been about!

"John, I'll go into St Andrews tomorrow," she said on the way home. "Someone will have handed them in to the police station."

Anne has great faith in human nature. If everyone was as honest as she is, all lost property would end up with the police.

I'll never forget the time I was trying to get our car into a small space in a car park in St Andrews. Anne had got out to help me reverse and, all of a sudden, she held up both arms.

"Stop, John." She stood in front of the bonnet. "Stop!"

I slammed on the brakes and Anne bent down to pick up a wet, bedraggled teddy bear. She got back into the car holding the wee mite.

"Some bairn will be crying their eyes out, John."

We agreed we should take it straight to the police station.

A lassie in a police uniform came to take down the particulars.

One teddy with blue bow, she wrote carefully, her face serious.

He looked so lost and lonely, sitting on that polished counter . . . I could see Anne would have liked to adopt him!

Anne had been asked to leave her name and address in case the teddy bear wasn't reunited with his owner. The police lassie explained that, if it wasn't claimed within six months, they would send us a postcard and Anne could go to collect it.

About four days later we received a letter. It was from a five-year-old,

helped by Mummy.

Thank you for my dear teddy. I cried and cried, but now we both go to bed together again.

Anne shed a tear.

"I told you, didn't I, that someone would go looking for him?"

To be honest, I'm just as soft as Anne is. It put me in mind of the time when, a week before Christmas, I was in the post office in Cupar.

As you go in, there are telephone boxes on the right. There was something inside one. I opened the door for a closer look and saw a packet of ladies' tights. I felt sorry for the lassie who'd been making a phone call and dropped one of her Christmas presents . . .

I took my find up to the police station, sure that some young lady would come to claim it. Six months later we got a postcard saying no-one had made a claim. Could we collect?

The next time we were in Cupar I drove Anne to the police station. She came out with the packet and got back into the car to open it.

How we both laughed!

No wonder they hadn't been collected. Some lassie had bought a new pair of tights, changed, and stuffed the torn pair in the box and dropped them on the floor of the telephone box!

I'll never live that good deed down . . .

But what about Anne's best gloves? Had she lost them for ever when they fell off her knees in St Andrews?

Not at all. She'd put them in the airing cupboard to dry out . . . ■

The Key To Success

I have everything all locked up.
Now all I need is the key . . .

WHEN we took over the farm all those years ago, we had two keys. One for the back door and one for the front.
The keys were massive. The one for the front door was hardly ever needed – only for important events like a funeral or a wedding. Before the war, we often went away and never locked the back door. If we did, you could have easily found the key under a very old curling stone close by.

Now we have keys for everything. I'll never forget when Anne managed to become immobile years ago. She hadn't lost a key – she could see it all right – she just couldn't get at it.

I couldn't go, that Sunday morning, to Kingsbarns Church, as a cow was calving. Anne was happy to go on her own in her wee car.

Anne had spotted the vehicle at a garage, liked the colour, and bought it.

When her grandsons saw it they were over the moon. Did Granny know what she had bought? To Anne it was just another car.

They explained to her that the black line round the bottom meant it had a "souped-up" engine.

"Gran, you'll have no trouble 'doing a ton'."

It was explained to us ignorant mortals that "doing a ton" meant doing 100 miles per hour. Gran never, when I was with her, touched a ton, but on a good road 70 was nothing to her.

Well, she took it to church that Sunday morning and when she came out, she couldn't find the key. She did note, however, that the key was in the right place – in the ignition – but all the doors were locked.

A couple of farmers tried to get a window open, but to no avail. In the end, one of them asked her if she had another set of keys at home.

"Yes," Anne said.

Anne told me later that the farmer had told her off for not saying so before. They had been struggling for half an hour and it was only 10 minutes to our farm to get the key.

"I did feel a fool," Anne said over lunch.

We bought a new car. A rare event, but we were due one.

The garage gave us two sets of keys – Anne put one lot into her bag and I keep the working set, but now I've lost mine.

I spent hours looking for them. As Anne says, I can't have lost them, only misplaced them.

I hate looking for anything and that key is a mystery. I must ring the garage and order three more sets.

I'm worried it might have dropped out of my pocket on to the hay, as I've hardly one pair of trousers that hasn't a hole in its pockets. I would hate a bullock to swallow it.

Anne and I once went to a wedding in that most delightful north of England town, Kirkby Lonsdale, on the banks of the River Lune.

We stayed at the hotel in the square. In those days it was full of antiques, but on a wall, as you entered, was an arrangement of keys which really took Anne's fancy.

There we saw eight large keys on the top row, six slightly smaller keys on the next row, and so on with a very wee one at the bottom.

Anne started collecting keys to make a similar design for our passage. She really made a very interesting design of them hanging on wee tacks.

Mind you, I wish the one for our new car was hanging there now! ▨

John and Anne enjoy a farm ball!

Domestic Bliss

TV Or No TV?

An unexpected visitor sent us jumping to the wrong conclusions . . .

WONDER if Mary will be going to the WRI meeting in Kingsbarns tonight?" Anne was asking the question aloud to herself, really. I knew why. If Mary was going, Anne would pick her up and they could have a good natter there and back.

"Ring her," I suggested.

Anne doesn't need a second invitation.

How long a chat it would be, I dread to think. I would ban farmers' wives – in the Riggin area, anyway – from getting on the phone from 7.30 a.m. to 10 a.m. The reason is simple. If I want to get hold of a fellow farmer to ask if he's sending a part-load of stock to auction, so we could share – or any other piece of urgent farming information – I find his line is always engaged!

Well, Anne rang Mary about the WRI meeting that night. Mary's husband was out at the byre so she unburdened herself.

No, she didn't think she had better go; she was in Ian's black books. Mary looks after the paperwork for the farm – all the tractor and car licences and any other bits of business.

Two men had arrived that morning at the back door in an odd kind of van.

"We're here to inspect your television licence, madam."

Ian had seen the van and come to find out what the men wanted. They repeated the request to him.

Ian is a rather blunt fellow, and is over six feet tall and about 15 stone. Mary said that he'd looked them up and down.

"The police have been warning us about the likes of you. Where's your identity cards?"

The two of them, so Mary said, whipped out cards with photos, saying they were from whoever looks after television licences.

Ian asked them in whilst Mary went to find the licence. Give Mary her due, she found the form, all filled in, and the cheque for the licence behind a china dog on the mantelpiece. They had never been posted.

It seems the form had come about three weeks in advance and Mary, being a careful sort, hadn't posted it right away. In the end she had forgotten all about it.

I met Ian in Cupar on the following Tuesday and promised to visit him in Perth Prison!

As soon as Anne came off the phone, she turned to me in a panic. "John, did you renew our TV licence?"

"No, dear, you did." To be honest, I wasn't certain, but if in doubt blame someone else. "You'd give a cheque, Anne, wouldn't you?"

Anne got out her cheque book stubs. No luck there – half of them weren't filled in.

In my little office-like place – the third bedroom – I went through the top drawer of my chest.

Oh, yes, I had television licences stamped and received for years back – but not this year's! Where was it? Had we ever applied for one?

You know how tempers can fray. Anne and I were now speaking to each other in tones which were not really in the harmony that loving people should use.

Do you put things away and remember at the time where you put them, but a couple of days later you haven't a clue?

Well, Anne didn't go to the meeting in Kingsbarns, either! We spent all evening searching!

Oh, yes, we had paid it. We don't know which of us did. I suspect Anne, as she had put it away (why, I don't know) in a drawer in the drum table in the sitting-room.

What did we do then? Switched on the TV – with a clear conscience! ▇

On The Right Track

It was curtains for me when Anne decided to do a spot of laundry!

I T was a Thursday morning, bright and crisp with a breeze blowing off the Forth. Anne was passing on her way to the bathroom when she picked up the bottom edge of the bedroom curtains.

"John Taylor, look at this."

Now, six a.m. isn't the time to ask me to look at a curtain. In any case, I didn't know why I was looking.

I was told it was filthy, with me rubbing against it on the way to the bathroom. I couldn't see it, but a kitchen chair was brought up by Anne even before I had got dressed.

Curtains were down and in the washing machine before I had time to mash a cup of tea.

"Good drying day," was Anne's description of the morn.

Nevertheless, I noticed she listened with a bit more interest than usual to the weather forecast.

You should also know I'd been hinting for a while that it would be a welcome change to have a piece of lamb one lunchtime.

As you know, I like my grub, and Anne has a constant battle to keep my weight down. So I was rather taken aback to come in for lunch and be greeted with a very welcome smell of roast.

I said nothing and waited.

As we were finishing lunch, Anne asked if I would go up to our bedroom, as she wanted my advice. When we reached that hallowed room – "John, I was wondering about moving the bed to there."

I should tell you our dear bed is big, king-size, heavy – the very devil to move. It's been where it is for over 50 years.

I had to explain to Anne that if she put it in that particular corner, she would have to crawl over me to get out.

"Well, what about there?"

"Darling, if you put it there, how will you get at the plug fittings? Why move it now?"

I learned that it was to save her washing the curtains again.

Anne was going to upset the whole tenor of our bedded lives for a curtain. I did note that I could gain two feet on my side by moving a chest on Anne's side the other way round. I pushed the king-size bed and nearly strained my back.

"You will keep to the left side, won't you, John?"

Murder has been committed for less.

It didn't rain and the curtains dried sufficiently for Anne to iron.

Cold lamb with mint sauce, creamed potatoes and leeks in a white sauce for tea. Anne knows how to oil the works.

Would I hang them? On the top of the pelmet are seven mugs, antiques, plus two old-fashioned soap-holders. I insisted that these be removed before I attempted to get those hook things on to the little runners. If one ornament had dropped off, you can guess the wrath that would have been poured on my head.

I hung the first curtain – well, not quite.

"I've four hooks and only one hanger."

"How stupid can a man be?" When they were last hung, that very morning, whoever put them up must have just forgotten to hang four hooks. I should have done the same.

"John, they won't hang right."

I suppose we all have a big box in which we keep everything which might come in handy. Down it came, and after opening tins containing buttons, nails and oddments, I found four hangers, thank goodness.

The curtains were up, so were the mugs, and there was still room for me to go to the bathroom without catching the curtain.

I suppose you could say I lost the battle and Anne won it, as usual! ▨

Another Fine Mess . . .

It's panic stations at the Riggin, but will I get the blame?

MUST be getting older because I find that a small upset I could take in my youth without a worry now becomes a burden.

I should be in bed. Anne's there, asleep, with the light above the bed full on. Why I'm not beside her, but sitting here mulling over today's to-dos, is simple to explain.

A couple who live in a cottage not far from us were away from home for a night, but when they returned they discovered their cottage had been burgled. The outcome of this episode was that Anne decided we should get an alarm system.

I went to the police station in St Andrews and they gave me a list of firms that install burglar alarm systems.

"Take estimates," Anne told me. "Don't commit yourself before we get an idea of prices."

Well, I did as she said and got in touch with three firms. They all sent surveyors and they all claimed to have the best systems.

To be honest, their prices were all about the same. I checked on the three quotes and chose one of them.

The firm who were putting in the system rang up a few days later.

"Could we come tomorrow?" Anne said yes, that would be fine.

"They'll be here tomorrow morning at eight," she told me after putting down the phone.

I smiled. Anne is nothing if not optimistic. They had to come from Dundee and if they arrived on the Riggin before ten, I'd be very surprised.

Well, when they did arrive – at eleven, I may add – they both went over the house and decided where they'd put their little boxes.

All systems, whether they be alarms or plumbing, seem to have to start in and come down from the attic.

Later in the day there was a cry from one of the workmen upstairs. He'd drilled through a water pipe. It was panic stations after that.

Oh, yes, we turned the water off, but not before the carpet in the

bathroom was soaking wet.

One good thing about living in a rural area is that the tradesmen are your friends. I rang our plumber, who lives in a nearby village.

"Oh, John, I don't know where he is; he has ten jobs on his round in St Andrews. Give me ten minutes," his wife told me.

Before the ten minutes were up, she'd phoned me back.

"John, I've found him in Boarhills. He'll be with you soon."

And so he was. Soon everything was back in order again. You can take it from me; the bill will go to the alarm firm. John Taylor didn't put a drill through that water pipe.

The mess made from putting in the alarm really annoyed Anne. But I don't see how the poor lad could have helped it – I kept telling Anne he'd clear up afterwards.

There are different ways of cleaning up and Anne's includes wiping down the walls, tops of pictures and doors, dusting all the furniture and taking the vacuum over the floor. To my simple mind, doing a spring clean because the poor lad made a bit of dust.

"Why did you think we needed an alarm system?" were Anne's last words before going to bed.

I said what I'd learned over 50 years was expected of me.

"Darling, if I'd known it was going to cause you so much trouble, I wouldn't have bothered." ■

Kitchen Sink Drama

I was certain there would be trouble when Anne got home – and I was right!

I **WAS** dreading Anne coming home last night. I knew I'd get the telling-off of my life. She'd gone off to Perth for the day with two friends who are interested in antiques and house furnishings.

There used to be 19 antiques shops in Perth – I know, I counted them once. If anything went wrong, I was told, I could ring the Royal George Hotel. They had planned to have an open sandwich and a cup of coffee there at lunchtime.

Now what, I'd thought scornfully, did she think would go wrong?

Well, something did go wrong. But I didn't ring my dear Anne!

Instead, I got her a good supper and laid our kitchen table properly to try to soften the blow which I knew was bound to fall on my head.

It happened like this . . .

Just after five I came into the kitchen. I'd been spreading dung on a meadow and I know I should have gone to the bathroom and had a bath. But I'm not a great bath man.

So I just took my shirt off – thank goodness I kept my trousers on – and was having a really good swill at the kitchen sink when there was a knock on the back door.

I was bending over the sink washing my hair, so I just shouted, "Come in!"

The door opened and in walked Her Ladyship. No, not Anne – the wife of our landlord.

"John, I thought my Andrew was the only one that washed in the kitchen sink!" she exclaimed. "I must tell him you do, too."

She's one of those ladies you can talk to, so I gave myself a rub down whilst she sat, not in the chair, but dangling her legs over the table.

"Your Ladyship, if you've come to ask Anne to relieve you of some turkey poults, you're not on."

If you have never tried to rear turkeys, you will never know the trials and tribulations involved! Lucky you!

How she laughed.

"No, John. I wouldn't inflict them on my best friend. I gave up rearing the darn things when your Anne did."

"Anne's gone to Perth but should be back any minute. Will you stay for supper?"

"Sorry, John, I have to get back. But thanks all the same."

"Can I give Anne a message?"

"I'll ring her, John." With a wave, she and her Land-Rover sped out of our yard.

Ten minutes later, Anne Taylor drove fast into the yard. I knew by the speed and her walk across the yard that yours truly was for it.

The door opened – and the storm began.

Anne had run into Her Ladyship up the lane and had been told that she had caught me with my pants down – or rather, shirt off.

It had amused Her Ladyship, but not my Anne.

"Can't you be left on your own without disgracing me?"

As we all came out of Kingsbarns Church on Sunday morning, Her Ladyship said in a stage whisper, "See you've got your shirt on this morning, John."

That – as you can guess – did not help matters with Anne. Never mind, it will always be one of those moments that I'll never forget! ■

Mr Fix-it

**If at first you don't succeed,
just keep plugging away!**

ANNE was sitting in her Orkney chair, apparently absorbed in her own thoughts, when suddenly she started to laugh so much that tears rolled down her cheeks.

I looked at her in astonishment, wondering what on earth she was laughing at.

Needless to say, it was me.

"John, you really are hopeless," she said at last as she wiped tears from her eyes.

I felt it was rather a sweeping statement. Surely I can't be that hopeless. After all, with Anne's help, I've run a farm, brought up two bairns, who are now a credit to us, paid my way, made a living and don't owe a soul a penny.

It turned out that what Anne was referring to was the fact that I'm hopeless with my hands.

The week before she had bought a new kettle and asked me to fit a plug to it. Some hours later I still hadn't managed to fix it to the kettle.

Fortunately that same evening a nephew came to see us. He's a farmer, too, but really good with his hands.

I took him into the dairy, away from Anne's prying eyes, and asked him to look at the plug. It was a great relief when he managed to put it right.

After Anne had stopped laughing I explained to her why I never learned about these things.

When I was a boy, we had oil lamps and candles for going to bed. Later on, however, we acquired a gas lamp. This lamp had a kind of gas mantle and a pump in the wee tank at the bottom which had to be primed.

There was a very thin wire on a handle with which you cleared the jet between tank and mantle.

Woe betide you if you didn't and ended up as my father did one Sunday afternoon in the kitchen.

There was an unearthly bang, the top blew off, then ignited all the clothes on the kitchen pulley.

Oh, we did get electricity eventually, but I'm afraid I was long past wanting to know how it worked.

Well, to come back to why Anne was laughing that night.

For the last 10 years or so, there has been a hood over the cooker with a filter which, when you switch it on, is meant to absorb the smells and steam. Anne's been on for a while about changing the filter.

"It must be full of grease," she keeps telling me.

I did look at it and got as far as trying to unscrew the darned thing. No go – I could feel I'd just break it.

One of our grandsons came to stay the night. He's just my opposite – very good with his hands.

He had the guard below the filters off in a jiffy. He then read a notice. The plastic case should be taken off the filters before use.

Well, well, we'd been switching it on in hope for about 10 years and it wasn't doing any good.

Now we knew why – the plastic case was still on.

Anne can blame me if she likes, but as an electrician installed it in the first place, how was I to know it wasn't right?

However, in her eyes, that and the incident with the kettle just go to show how hopeless I am, and I think we all know that she'll never let me live them down. ▥

A Job Well Done

. . . brings its own rewards, I always say.

ANNE had an aunt, now long departed, who always lectured her on keeping the stone slab area at her back door clean.

She told Anne to get down on her hands and knees, on an old sack, and scrub with a brush and washing soda. The reason for this was, according to the aunt, because Anne would never get a man unless she kept her back door spotlessly clean!

Why the back door? Well, on farms in our area, no-one went to the front door. That was kept for weddings and funerals.

Anne did as instructed and, of course, she did get a man, even if it was only John Taylor.

She didn't catch me because she scrubbed her back doorstep, though. To be honest, I never really noticed it. However, I suppose I would have done if there'd been some old buckets, a jam jar or two and other bits and pieces lying around.

I can always remember their back door. There was a wide but low door frame which I had to duck under as I went in. I'm telling you this as Anne has always followed the advice of her maiden aunt and kept both front and back doors not only clean, but the doors and surrounds freshly painted.

Anne's very fussy when it comes to anything around the house. Not that I mind. I'm proud, as you can guess, of how Anne has made it a real homely home, if you get what I mean.

I came in for lunch one day in early June and found Anne in a real state. She'd been out through the front door looking at the garden, and on the way back she'd noticed that because of the heat, the boards in the door had parted and the paint had likewise left a big gap.

"What shall I do?" she asked helplessly. "Send for the painter, dear, and get it touched up."

The painter duly arrived and did the necessary to the front door.

"Oh, Mr Anderson, while you're here, can you give me a price for papering the hall and passage?" Anne inquired when he had finished.

"Do you want the paper stripped off?" he asked.

Anne looked at me.

I kept quiet.

"That would be very expensive," he went on.

Mr Anderson, who, it was obvious, didn't want to have to strip the paper off, suggested a thick paper to cover up the paper underneath.

I agreed but said nothing.

He gave a cost for doing the work.

"But," he added, "I'm afraid you'll have to add the cost of the paper, Mrs Taylor."

Anne, give her her due, doesn't paper, or rather repaper, every second year like some people I know. In fact, the passage area now under threat of repapering hasn't been done for more years than I care to remember. A careful sort, my Anne.

Now the trouble started. The painter sent three books of samples.

Anne spread them out on the kitchen table. I looked, or flicked, through one book and chose a paper.

"How do you like that?"

Anne mumbled, "Mmm," and continued to go through the book slowly, page by page.

If she said, "How do you like that?" once, she said it 50 times. I almost lost my temper.

"Darling, just choose one and order it," I said, exasperated.

Anne didn't seem to notice my feelings.

"Shall I send for more books, dear?" she asked innocently.

At that point, I left the kitchen and went into the byre. No cow was calving, but if I'd stayed with Anne any longer I'd have lost my temper.

Eventually, Anne picked a paper and I agreed it was just right. Thank goodness for that.

I was fast asleep when I got a dig in the ribs.

"John, do you think I've chosen the right paper?"

At two in the morning, it was too much to take; I ignored her, rolled over and went straight back to sleep. ▥

It's A Date

Will I forget an anniversary?
Not if Anne can help it . . .

ARE you asleep?"

Time – about five a.m. Place – one large double bed and Anne asking the question.

"Yes, why, dear?"

"What day is it?"

"Tuesday."

"I know that, but what date is it, John?"

"Well, you said if your aunt Edna had lived till last Tuesday, she would have been a hundred and seven . . ."

"What's that got to do with today's date?"

"Well, last Tuesday was her birthday and it was always on the nineteenth."

I could sense that Anne, on her fingers, under the bedclothes, was counting: Tuesday the nineteenth, Wednesday the twentieth, etc., till she came to the conclusion it was the twenty-sixth.

"John, it's about time you pulled your weight."

I was more interested in pulling the bedclothes my way.

"If it's the twenty-sixth, it's our Mary's and Ian's wedding anniversary next Saturday. It's time you took over the remembering of birthdays and anniversaries. Why should it always be me?"

"You like doing them, dear."

"Only because you are too lazy to remember."

"I put them all in the diary."

I knew what the outcome to that remark would be.

"Fat lot of good in the diary! It wants to be on a card."

I switched the transistor on, much to Anne's annoyance. There's news on the World Service at five a.m.

"Shut that thing off, I want to go to sleep."

The way Anne said it you'd think I was the one who had started the discussion in the first place.

I thought I did pull my weight or, rather, do my bit over birthdays.

Every year I buy a large diary. It has three days to a page and lots of empty pages to put all sorts of notes in. You would really laugh at some of the entries.

Most important is my entry of my weight at six a.m. every morning. As soon as this diary arrives, I sit down at my desk and transfer 19 birthday dates plus two anniversaries from our very ancient address book. That's so we don't forget. What more can I do?

I can hear Anne saying, "Do? Buy the cards, write them, put stamps on and post them, that's what you could do!"

That wouldn't be fair on her, though. She's always done it since we married. It would be taking away one of her great pleasures in life.

I take the dates from the last tattered page in our address book. We started it soon after we married. It's a sorry sight now, but still a good and faithful friend. The back is there, but on the point of falling off.

I hope we hadn't many friends whose names started with A. The A page is missing and so are the first lot of Bs.

The three back pages are interesting. All sorts of notes written, some upside-down, as Anne has taken a message over the telephone.

We go through the address book each Christmas to see we haven't missed anyone we should have remembered. We really should get a new one, but it wouldn't be the same as this friendly old book we have thumbed through for years.

As I came in for my cup of beef tea and nothing else at nine a.m. that same morning, I shouted from the porch where I was taking my wellies off.

"Darling, it's Mary's anniversary on Saturday."

As I opened the kitchen door, I was met by a wet dish cloth which hit me in the chest. Anne has quite a good aim.

You see – every time I try to pull my weight, Anne just throws hers around! ▦

Crystal Clear!

Anne saw through my attempt to sweep my mistake under the carpet . . .

ANNE has a number of sayings that she comes out with from time to time.

If she is feeling in a really daft mood while we are washing up, out will come – in a sing-song voice – "John, does your mother take in washing – oh, no, she keeps a tripe shop."

We both laugh. It's such a daft saying, and Anne has no idea where she got it from.

I don't suppose there are many now who take in washing to keep the wolf from the door, and I'm certain there are no tripe shops in Scotland.

I didn't really set off to go into the merits of tripe, but now that I mention it, I'm a great tripe and onions fan.

If your wife ever says no to tripe – because it needs hours and hours of cooking – tell her she doesn't know her onions. She might have been right in her young day, but things have moved on a bit since then.

Supermarkets nowadays have twigged that if they want to sell tripe, they must part-cook it. So that's what they do. It still needs cooking, but only a moderate amount.

Take my advice – don't just go and buy a pound of tripe, buy three pounds. Add an equal amount of onions – you won't find that in any cookery book, but I love onions!

The reason for the three pounds is that you should eat half hot the first day, and if you put the rest into a bowl, it will set beautifully. You can have it cold next day or heat it up.

Well, what I set out to tell you about was one of Anne's famous sayings: "Be sure your sins will find you out."

She came out with that one this morning. My fault, as usual.

Anne, as I've told you, is a great collector of things for the house. She used always to be taking the buggy and going off to the sales.

She had a fascination for wine glasses. Why, I don't know, because Anne, like me, has no idea about wine.

Once she bought a really beautiful corner cupboard.

"To put my glasses in," she told me when I asked.

And in they went, but, oh, we had a job to get them all in, and if you sneezed they rattled.

Anne, bless her, enjoys company, and we often invite friends round on a Saturday night. So two farming couples were invited.

Anne instructed me to give them a drink.

"Give them all a sherry, John. Don't ask what they would like. Eric would drink a whole bottle of whisky given half a chance."

So sherries all round it was. Eric didn't half give me a look, though.

Well, I washed up after they had gone and put the crystal sherry glasses into the wee space allowed for them in Anne's new corner cupboard.

In so doing – disaster – I knocked a beautiful wine glass on to the floor, where it broke into atoms.

Listening to see if Anne had heard, I hurriedly picked up the pieces and put them in an envelope.

On my way back from Cupar auction on the Tuesday, I came via St Andrews and replaced my broken wine glass.

End of story? Not quite.

About a month later, Anne was doing her usual inspection of the carpet in the parlour – for moths.

"John, there are wee bits of glass on the floor . . ."

Well, I had to own up, didn't I? My face gave the game away.

How Anne laughed, and said the immortal line, "Be sure your sins will find you out."

Mine certainly did. And Anne's promised I'll be anything but immortal if I do it again. ▮

Read All About It

I am convinced I'm in the right, for once . . .

D **ARLING,** can you help me?"

When Anne says "darling" you can guess she wants something. I had just come in from the evening's milking for a wash and then a well-earned high tea.

"Our Mary's been on the phone and she wants me to go to some horse trials on Saturday."

"That'll be nice for you."

I'm not what you would call a horse-trial fan. Still, lots of youngsters, plus adoring parents, get great pleasure, or sometimes disappointment, out of them, so who am I – humble John Taylor – to belittle them?

Our grandsons have done well at the trials in the past.

"Mary says there was a bit about it in today's 'Courier'. I read it, but can't find it now and she told me to read it so that I would know all about it before we went.

"Could you please find the piece in 'The Courier' for me?"

Well, that Friday's "Courier" had 26 pages. The paper was in bits since Anne had gone through each page then let it fall to the floor.

I picked up the pages at random and studied them, but found no mention of any horse trials.

I looked at the page numbers – pages five and six were missing.

Anne found them, but still we had no luck as far as the article we were looking for was concerned.

I hate to be beaten, even over not being able to find something in the newspaper – blood pressure rises, temper gets frayed and you bark at your wife, which doesn't solve the problem.

I got on the floor, laid out page one and page twenty-six, then put every other page in its right place – all 26 pages were there. I straightened them out, pressed them and sat at our whitewood kitchen table to pore over them.

Had Anne seen it in an advert? I went through them on the front and back pages.

Answer – no. I scanned every single item but, no, it wasn't there.

"I read it this morning."

"Darling, it isn't in today's paper."

You can guess the arguments between us. Why is it that two people who really love each other get all het up and fall out, nearly to the point of walking out, over something which doesn't really matter?

Well, Anne and I got to that stage on that Friday night. Neither of us likes to be beaten.

I picked up my bonnet and went down the yard to look at the lambing ewes. One ewe was having difficulties. Jip and I went to investigate.

I caught it, poor soul, and found the lamb had its legs back. I won't trouble you with the details of how I got it the right way for coming into this world, but I did and, with the ewe's help, a beautiful ram lamb came into the world.

I got it to suck and left them happy.

I sat on the big stone looking out to the Forth, watching the boats going up and down this famous Scottish channel. And slowly it dawned on me what had happened with Anne and her reading about the horse trials – it wasn't that day's paper.

We save every piece of paper and box them for the St Andrews Boys' Brigade to sell for their funds.

As I came back from the ewes, I went into the dairy where we box the papers, and took out the last three days' "Couriers".

Oh, yes, I found it – Thursday's paper. Anne had read it and there it was – a long story about the horse trials.

I took it in to Anne and placed it on the kitchen table.

"Sorry, John, but thanks."

Do you ever feel sure, as Anne did, that you read something in the daily papers that day, but later find out it was in an earlier edition? I have to confess, it happens to me, too.

We all make mistakes, but don't like to admit it. ▦

A Clean Sheet

Anne's had an idea, and it's not good news for me!

ANNE pulled the curtains back. Time – six-thirty a.m. The sunlight streamed through.

It was one of those crisp, clear mornings in spring that we get in Fife, when you can see right across the Forth to North Berwick. Mind you, I couldn't even see the Forth, as I was still under the bedclothes!

Anne pulled the window open, letting all the cold March air in, turned round quickly, grasped the bed covers and whipped them away.

"Get up, John Taylor, it's a day for washing blankets."

I never did agree with this spring-cleaning bug. Anne's mother always said that if you kept your house clean throughout the year there was no need to rush around like a mad hare in the spring.

Sounds like common sense to me, but once Anne's mind's made up . . . No peace for the wicked, so I had to move.

I must admit, despite all, looking out of the window was a beautiful experience – the land falling away to Anstruther, the May island sitting there like a battleship, Berwick Law in the background of that lovely morning.

We just have a cup of something before I go across to the byre.

"Oh, John, be a dear and put the line up on your way."

Anne always says "be a dear" when she wants something done.

I was handed the clothes-line, plus a damp cloth to wipe it.

By the time I came back for my breakfast, blankets, sheets, a long bolster and some pillow-cases were enjoying the breeze from off the Forth. Anne had been busy.

Mind you, the work involved in doing the washing now is nothing compared with when Anne was a girl. In those days, someone would get up at half-past five in the morning, fill the copper boiler in the wash-house from the pump in the yard and then light the fire under the boiler.

It was a very wee fire grate and you had to keep stoking it with wood till the water boiled. Hard work indeed.

Dependent on the day, sometimes the sheets went on the line, sometimes on the grass, where they were supposed to dry whiter.

Anyway, we had nearly finished our usual very tasty breakfast when: "John, are you really busy?" Anne asked.

"Not really. I'm going to look at the ewes on the top land."

"They won't die if you're half an hour late, will they?"

What Anne was getting round to was, would I give her a hand with the bed. What could I say but, "Yes, dear."

Give Anne her due, when she makes up her mind to do a job, she does it thoroughly; sometimes, in my eyes, a bit too thoroughly.

Well, it's a big bed – six and a half feet long and five feet across. Anne said we might as well strip it right down as I was helping.

Off came the electric blanket. Underneath seemed hundreds of buttons. Stiff brush and dustpan came into play as each button was cleaned for dust.

Next we needed a big heave as we turned the mattress and the brushing was repeated on the other side. Then came the re-making. Electric blanket, an old under-blanket, an under-sheet and then a big sheet.

Then the tucking-in process – just as they do in hospital. I didn't know there was a wrong way to put a pillow in its case, but there is, so Anne said, and I got it wrong – trust me!

I can see why she often suggests we get a downie!

We then had to put on another sheet, two blankets, an eiderdown and a top cover!

"Thanks, dear – like a cup of tea?"

We sat with two mugs and elbows on the kitchen table. I never knew that "changing the bed" was such a wearisome task. ▪

Sleeping Sickness

That's what I have, according to my Anne!

I'M in trouble again. Anne had said good night and gone upstairs. There was no reason I could think of why she should come down again, but she did, just in time to catch me making a cheese sandwich.

Did she give me what for! Cheese, indeed, at that time of night. Had I no respect for her?

I would get into bed, put my head on the pillow, fall asleep and snore and snore and snore – so Anne said.

Well, I have a lot of respect for my darling Anne, but I do like a cheese sandwich. I don't think a wee snack before bed has any effect on my snoring one way or another.

For some reason, these days, I tend to wake up somewhere between two and three o'clock in the morning.

Sometimes I take a walk down the passage, but other times I just lie awake waiting for the grandfather clock in the hall to strike three. Then I turn over and try to get to sleep.

"John, are you awake?" Anne will ask.

On ascertaining that is the case, she then proceeds to give me a lecture.

"Please, John, stay awake for ten minutes so that I can get to sleep. You've snored all night and I haven't had a wink."

Anne came back from tea with some friends with the news that Rina, a lady at the coffee morning, had told the others how she had managed to cure her husband of snoring.

He only snored when he lay on his back, so she sewed a cotton reel to the collar of his pyjamas so it hung down his back. If he rolled over on to his back, the bobbin woke him.

"John, what do you think about that?" Anne asked me with a wee twinkle in her eye.

She soon found out what I thought. I told her that if she dared to try any silly trick like that she would have a cold bed all to herself!

She gave me a dig in the tummy one night, complaining that she hadn't been to sleep for my snoring. Would I try to keep awake for just a few minutes whilst she got to sleep?

I started to climb out of bed.

'Where are you going?" she asked.

"Into the spare bed."

"Oh, no, you don't," she told me. That bed had been made up, all turned back just right and, snore or no snore, I wasn't to disturb her handiwork.

So I can't win.

Have you got into a routine of sleeping on a particular side of your double bed? If you stand at the bottom of our bed, I sleep on the right and am on my right shoulder.

I'm on the window side of our bedroom. We always sleep with it open, so I get the draught on my back.

When we are away, and that's not often, we always have difficulty in working out which side of the bed we should get in. The window is never in the right place.

We went to London once, to Smithfield Market, and came back on the sleeper. Have you ever tried to sleep two in one of those wee beds you get on British Rail?

If not, don't try – it wasn't the most comfortable night's sleep I've had and we were a lot younger then.

I always say it's important to make sure your sleeping arrangements are ideal.

After all, you spend a third of your life doing it. ■

Anne's kitchen is the heart of the Taylors' home.

Published in Great Britain by D.C. Thomson & Co., Ltd., 185 Fleet Street, London EC4A 2HS
© D.C. Thomson & Co. Ltd. 2018
Tel. 01382 223 131
www.dcthomson.co.uk